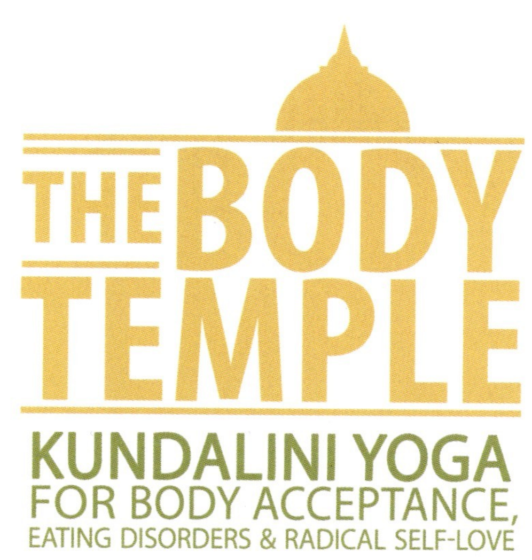

RAMDESH KAUR

Spirit Voyage
Purcellville, VA 20132
1-888-735-4800 • www.SpiritVoyage.com

Photos by Gurusurya Khalsa
Edited by Sat Purkh Kaur Khalsa and Sahib-Amar K. Khalsa
KRI Review by Siri Neel Kaur Khalsa
Musical Annotations by Ram Dass Khalsa
Design & Layout by Prana Projects, Ditta Khalsa and Biljana Nedelkovska

This publication has received the KRI Seal of Approval.

This seal is only given to products that have been reviewed for accuracy and integrity of the sections containing 3HO lifestyle teachings and Kundalini Yoga as taught by Yogi Bhajan®.

The ideas, procedures, and suggestions in this book are not intended as a substitute for the medical advice of a trained health professional. All matters regarding your health require medical supervision. Consult your physician before adopting the suggestions in this product, as well as about any condition that may require diagnosis or medical attention. The author and publisher disclaim any liability arising directly of indirectly from the use of this product.

Published 2016
Library of Congress Cataloging-in-Publication Data
Name: Ramdesh Kaur, 1979 - author
Title: The Body Temple: Kundalini Yoga for Body Acceptance, Eating Disorders, and Radical Self-Love / Ramdesh Kaur
Description: Purcellville, VA : Spirit Voyage, 2016 | Includes bibliographical references
Identifiers: LCCN 2016941545 | ISBN-13: 978-0-9835695-3-4 (softcover)
Subjects: LCSH: Kundalini. | Yoga.

MODELS

Ramdesh Kaur
Christa Mastrangelo Joyce
Theresa Anne Voellinger
Gurusurya Khalsa
Harnam
Deanna Stoika
Jen Rolston
Halie Kupinski
Kalyn Cocker
Janet Marie Pasiuk

Special thanks to Jala Yoga, Shepherdstown, West Virginia
jalayogaflow.com

DEDICATION

To my spiritual teacher, Yogi Bhajan, for these teachings that touch my soul.

To Harnam the Magnificent, for more reasons that I can count.

And to my Body Temple, who stayed with me through every length of this journey, supported me even while I ignored its needs, and ultimately taught me how to love myself in the most radical and extraordinary way. I bow to your wisdom, your strength, and your beautiful human grace.

Contents

Foreword

Dr. Kathy Milano, PhD

I sat with an intelligent, creative young woman one day as she told me about a recent date with a man she was seeing. It was the perfect weather for lunching outdoors with an interesting man who had everything going for him in terms of appearance, intelligence, and worldly success. Upon returning from the restroom, this woman was taken aback when offered an unsolicited assessment of her face and body from this accomplished plastic surgeon. With generous intent, her date offered his expert opinion about how she could go about fixing every flaw in order to maximize her beauty. In the poignant silence that followed this story, witnessing the tears flowing down the most lovely face, I had one question: "Why didn't you keep walking?"

With every story you hear, you are offered the choice to listen from afar or dive within to find yourself in the characters and the play. I invite you to dive in and honestly explore how this common storyline has appeared time and time again in your own life. To examine where you were told you were imperfect and where, in response, you kept walking or were stopped in your tracks.

Within society at large and your intimate subculture, you repeatedly encounter gross and subtle messages directing you to alter your flawed appearance or behavior in order to present yourself in a more acceptable manner. Parents, teachers, friends, institutions, self-help experts, and media offer their well-meaning or indifferent advice about how to become more attractive, successful, or pleasing to have around. From a young age, this barrage of unsolicited advice is so insidious that it finds a home within you, masquerading as your own voice. Unfortunately, this conditioned, internalized voice joins forces with societal influence to interrupt the development of a resilient, generous, and balanced sense of being which proclaims an unequivocal delight in its own unique beauty. Depending upon the nature of your specific life experience, traumas large and small, and models of self-acceptance or self-rejection, you may have partially or fully digested this unsavory invitation to correct your inadequacies.

This unfortunate side effect of growing up human in an imbalanced world may leave you struggling with an unsatisfied longing to be different than you are, a habit of self-loathing, self-destructive impulses masquerading as solutions, and an inevitable journey to heal what is broken.

The world in which you live and the mental constructs guiding your perception encourage an "outside in" approach to polishing that which has been tarnished. It is no surprise, then, that a storyline revealing the tainted core of humanity would result in a shared attempt to hide the imperfections and seek the next thing that will provide relief. This common story allows the inexplicable actions of self-diminishment and self-destruction to make perfect sense. From Häagen Dazs to heroin, from bingeing to purging, seeking to soothe the inner torment and quiet external critics may be understood compassionately as a strategy to feel accepted, loved, and valued. Every protective action, even those withholding self-acceptance or inciting self-harm, may be seen as an action taken in order to feel better in the moment. When you challenge society's "outside in" approach to healing by viewing disorders as "in orders," you may gently loosen the grip of shame that resides as a partner to your inner critical voice.

Going further, you see that the cultural approach to fixing imperfection rests firmly upon a foundational flaw. A limited understanding of the vital, precious life force energy, which wisely animates all things and restores that which is injured, has turned this healing focus inside out and upside down. In *The Body Temple*, Ramdesh is encouraging you to uncover this fatal flaw in order to turn your own healing journey inside out. Rather than seeing the practice of Kundalini Yoga as yet another method to fix what is broken, you are encouraged to challenge the idea of being broken altogether. As you explore the integrated parts of this Yoga of Awareness, you will find that rather than being encouraged to hide your flaws, you are empowered to free your life force energy. Ramdesh guides you methodically through a yogic practice that naturally challenges the pervading model of a flawed humanity to uncover an inner wellspring of strength.

As layers of conditioned beliefs, habits, and emotions are gradually released, you have the potential to realize that far from being tarnished, your innermost essence is whole, radiant, and beautiful. Directly experiencing the clarity of such life-enhancing energy through the practice of yoga is yours to explore.

No amount of description from others will substitute for your own unique experience of discovering what is within and how your own soul sings of a transformation that simply sheds all that is false. When you are bound by a belief in your inadequacy, what lies within—that shining jewel—may be beyond imagining. Whether it is the desire for a fuller experience of life or the desperate escape from pain that launches you onto the path of the hero, simply take the first step in this journey that will lead you to clarity about what matters most.

The hero's journey, filled with challenge, confusion, fear, and courage, is depicted beautifully in the Alice in Wonderland movie directed by Tim Burton. As Alice finds herself desperate to rescue the Mad Hatter from the Red Queen, she must solve the problem of her tiny size—the result of her previous shrinking. Reaching quickly for a tool of empowerment, the magical cake, Alice finds herself growing right out of her clothes. Towering above the garden, depending upon a large bush to cover her vulnerable nakedness, Alice faces the much feared Red Queen, who asks, "What happened to your clothes?" Alice matter-of-factly replies, "I outgrew them. I've been growing an awful lot lately." True transformation always requires the shedding of the beliefs, memories, and habits that bind you. This process, as Alice discovered, involves a lot of shrinking and stretching while other voices tell you what you must do and who you must be. Gradually, as you keep on walking, you quiet these inaccurate, disempowering voices so that you can hear the siren song of your soul that reveals the most amazing revelation of all: there was never anything wrong with you in the first place.

I had the privilege to travel alongside Ramdesh during one leg of her own hero's journey. During our time together, I witnessed her courage to go further within her center to explore and root out those false ideas and unhelpful habits that interfered with her alignment with her essential wholeness. Recognizing that life holds every joy and sorrow, we allowed everything to be witnessed, experienced, and released with understanding, self-compassion, and a commitment to continue upon her healing journey. Some time later I met Ramdesh and learned she had applied her capacity to dive in, deeply understand, and intelligently apply her knowledge to becoming a teacher of Kundalini Yoga. Most importantly, I noticed that an authentic radiance was emerging within her.

My introduction to the practice of Kundalini Yoga was unexpected. Nestled within a rustic cabin in a valley surrounded by the Colorado Rocky Mountains, I was looking forward to immersing myself in the sacred chants of Kundalini Yoga with the musician, Snatam Kaur. To my surprise, I had innocently entered a three-day Kundalini Yoga intensive. Breathing, moving, and chanting in this intimate setting, I directly experienced the transformative power of the many facets constituting the technology of Kundalini Yoga. What resonated most during my introduction to this potentially rigorous practice was Snatam's invitation to immerse ourselves in the practice at whatever level was available to us. Witnessing those who were unable to sit on the floor or complete the movements, Snatam explained the potential for this yogic technology to work while we were simply immersed within the sound current, breathing, and moving with intent in a way that honored the body's limitations. With this invitation, I let go. Truly letting go of any concern about doing things correctly, achieving any result, or understanding the depth of the practice, I found it easy to befriend myself as I was in each moment. My experience has continued to demonstrate the potential of the practice of Kundalini Yoga to release conditioning within the body, emotions, thoughts, and energy. I share Snatam's invitation as a complement to Ramdesh's encouraging voice so that you may move gently through these practices, honoring what serves your restorative healing journey. Not every practice is for everyone. Trust your innermost voice and share any concerns with your yoga teacher, therapist, or medical provider in order to ensure that you are well served by what is offered. You have choices here. Own your power and pace your journey. There is no race to the finish line.

"I believe in the beauty of your soul." This is what I said on a day long ago to that young woman who was so courageously committed to her path of healing. Knowing that today she, like Alice, has shed the harsh voice of the conditioned mind and deeply experiences the radiance of her essence speaks to a grace unfolding that deeply touches my heart. In *The Body Temple*, Ramdesh is sharing her genuine interest in your well-being, faith in your capacity to explore your unique path of healing, and the technology of Kundalini Yoga to ease your passage into wholeness. Finding the truth within requires a gradual shedding of any and everything hiding the brilliance of your inner wholeness. An exploration into self-acceptance, self-love, and healthy self-nourishment is a journey worth taking. As Ramdesh learned, it is a practical journey filled with moments of courageous opening and fearful cowering. Learning to befriend yourself along the way is an act of wisdom and self-compassion that acknowledges the challenging complexity of this wonderful, messy experience of being human. May you walk the hero's path with companions who see your preciousness, tools that help you shed your conditioned "clothing" of inadequacy, the siren song of your soul proclaiming your wholeness, and the growing realization that you have a right to be as you are simply because you exist. The world awaits the preciousness of your being and the gifts you have come to share. Keep on walking. Sat Nam.

Kathy Milano, PhD
KathyMilano.com

My body is a temple.

CHAPTER 1

Before You Begin

"If any thing is sacred the human body is sacred."

~ Walt Whitman

Many of you reading this book do not have an eating disorder, but some of you may. If you are in a severe active state of any eating disorder, at risk of self-harm, or a danger to yourself, please seek professional help. Throw this book into your bag on your way out the door, but it is imperative that if you are in crisis, you seek treatment now. Eating disorders are life-threatening, and there is nothing more precious than you, even if you don't realize it yet. The teachings and tools within this book are not meant to replace professional medical treatment; they are intended to support a meditative, spiritual journey that will support you in the long haul. Recovery from any addiction, including eating disorders, is a marathon, not a sprint. For some, these tools may be all you need to carve out a path to self-love and healing; for others they will be a key supplement.

If you think you aren't ready for help or don't want it, hear this: You Deserve to Be Happy. Read that again, because it is entirely true that you deserve a feeling-good life in a feeling-good body. You deserve to grow, to thrive, and to live your destiny. Your story may include an eating disorder or negative body image, but you are so much more than this one chapter. You can heal. You can emerge through this critical and challenging time and flower into the fullness of your heart. I know this to be true because it happened for me. I remember feeling that there was nothing past the cycle of binge and purge and restriction and self-punishment that I had been stuck in for years, that there was no way forward in life without it. I was very wrong. There is a whole world on the other side of recovery; and for me, I have to treat recovery like a close friend. We keep in touch. I don't just mean recovery from an eating disorder. I mean recovery from feeling uncomfortable in my own body, recovery from negative thoughts about my body and myself, and recovery from thinking that my body has to meet some ideal in order for my life to be good. I have to watch my thoughts every day, and stay vigilant in my self-love and self-care.

I actively use the teachings of Kundalini Yoga and Meditation to remind myself of my self-worth and to restore my spirit so that I don't fall back into unhealthy habits and patterns. To get here, in this healed and happy state, I did a lot of work, and I continue working. The majority of that work was Kundalini Yoga as taught by Yogi Bhajan® including lots of meditation and mantra. I also relied on psychotherapy, especially in the early stages of recovery. But in the end, I found that I couldn't count on anyone or anything outside of myself to heal. Only I could love myself, and only I could use the power of self-love to change my life. Only I could put the tools and techniques included in this book to use.

Some of what you read here might seem strange or different, especially if you haven't practiced Kundalini Yoga before. Some of the language in the meanings of the mantras might make you uncomfortable if you don't have a spiritual practice, but the truth is you do not have to believe in God for any of this to heal or to help. The only thing you have to believe in is yourself.

Let me say this: I believe you can heal, too. Whether you have an eating disorder or not, if you have ever had an unkind thought about yourself or your body, I am holding the space for you to thrive. With every word in this book, I hope to reach out across time and space and give you a hug. I know how it feels to have an eating disorder, but I also know how it feels to recover. I know what it's like to hate my body and punish it, and I know what it's like to love my body and adore it. Standing in the light feels so much better than keeping yourself trapped in the darkness.

Take my hand, open this book, and begin a journey to Feeling Good Again. The path of Kundalini Yoga has secrets to teach you, not the least of which is this: You are destined to *shine*.

With all my love, courage, and faith in you,
Ramdesh Kaur

My body is a safe place for my spirit to live.

CHAPTER 2

About My Journey

"Do you not know that your body is
the temple of the Spirit?"

~ 1 Corinthians 6:19

I believe that all of our lives are epic journeys; we are all embarking on an odyssey with adventures, battles, and siren calls, until at last we return home to our own soul. Some of us journey on routes that veer toward struggles with accepting our body, loving ourselves, and developing a positive relationship with food. Mine certainly has.

I don't identify with any eating disorder at this point in my life, but I have experienced them all: anorexia, bulimia, compulsive overeating, and orthorexia have all touched me in some way. Bulimia stayed with me the longest and left the greatest imprint, but it seems that part of my life's journey was to experience a bit of many different eating disorders and challenges with self-love so that I could know them from the inside and be able to offer help. Sometimes you have to be wounded for the light to enter you in a precise way so it can reflect back to others.

Although I can comfortably say that I have been well for years, I have also been extremely sick from my eating disorders. Accepting my body and loving the skin I'm in are daily opportunities to practice what I preach here in this book, so really, you and I are going on this journey to radical self-love together. Many books about eating disorders that I've read tend to share the details of their authors' stories as if the sadness of the story alone might encourage others. I don't think it works. I was the girl who went to the eating disorders group therapy sessions just to learn new strategies for losing more weight, so I won't share the brutal details of my story to be used in that way. But I will provide a brief history of myself and my body image.

At the sickest time of my life, during college, I was throwing up anywhere from 20 to 40 times a day. It was never about the food for me, or even about the lack of it. It was never even about my weight, even when I thought it was and obsessed over it every waking moment. My eating disorders were about not knowing how to handle the physical and mental stress that I felt within my body. I didn't know how to release excess energy, and I didn't know how to deal with my feelings of unworthiness and dissatisfaction. My spirit was hungry for something more.

Anorexia was about control and compliments and a cycle of self-denial. I might have felt worthless, but the more weight I lost the more other people validated my worth with their attention, smiles, or compliments. After being overlooked as a chubby teen, I became the center of attention as a starving woman. My bulimia grew from feeling utterly out of control. It began as a coping mechanism. I didn't yet understand how sensitive I was, and when I experienced stress and anxiety within, I had to find a way to get it out. Bingeing was ultimately about purging, and the nearly ecstatic feeling of relief after vomiting, which over time became a chemical addiction. Like all addictions, eventually I had to vomit just to function, to be able to think clearly or manage my life; it was no longer about reaching euphoria. Instead, I built my day around bathrooms and keeping secrets, and the damage I did to my body and mind during those times lasted the longest. Left with a hole where my self-worth should have been, I derived what little self-esteem I had from my ability to appear sexually attractive to men.

Compulsive overeating helped me stuff my emotions down when they became unmanageable. The first time I remember using that as a strategy was when I was very young. I would hide in the pantry and eat mindlessly in secret. Although I always had confidence in my intellectual abilities, my confidence in my physical form was always lacking. I needed nearly constant external validation in order to feel good, and didn't yet know how to make myself feel spiritually full from the inside out.

This isn't a chronological account, and many of these eating disorders overlapped each other. I went from one to another and back again at various intervals, like a pendulum swinging from one extreme to another. At some points it would seem as if I was getting better, but soon I would arrive at the other end of the extreme and begin to struggle with the opposite manifestation of my ultimate problem: a deep, core lack of self-esteem and self-love.

Many of you won't relate to these extremes, but you'll know what it's like to avoid your reflection in the mirror, to make a snide remark about your body under your breath, or to just never feel beautiful enough. I can relate to you there as well. After finding myself almost 100 pounds heavier than at my thinnest, I have also experienced the discomfort of a body that feels too heavy, too restrictive, and not the shape I desire. My mind even tried to convince me that I couldn't write this book until I was thin again. But I realized that I don't need to listen to or identify with thoughts like that, nor do I need to prove that I am healthy through dramatic weight loss in order to share my gifts—and neither do you.

So many times I hear from people who don't go to a yoga class because they feel intimidated; they are heavier, bigger, or less flexible than the ideal yogi, and many people quit before they even begin because they don't fit the mold. I won't let my body hold me back now, and I encourage you not to let yours hold you back either. You can do Kundalini Yoga and Meditation at any size, at any age, and at any level of physical fitness. You can also heal over and over again, at every level of your body, mind, and spirit. You don't ever have to be finished, because more growth is always possible.

I've often wondered why these challenges have been a part of my life experience. Likely there is some family programming there, some ancient karmic record from my ancestors who dealt with similar issues and passed them on. But I also think I never felt perfect because I didn't connect with my Spirit, and my body then felt like a cage, a prison, and I felt like something must be wrong with me for being in it.

I also believe that I came here to help you; if I had not lived within these challenges and issues I wouldn't be a suitable guide to help you or someone you know out of them. I needed to incarnate and live this karma so that I could learn how to find my way out and leave a trail for others to follow. If you have your own challenges with self-love and body image, I hope you leave a trail of healing behind you, too. There are too many of us struggling with feeling good in our bodies to leave a single person behind. We have to shift this for future generations so that one day no one grows up feeling like something is wrong with them or that they aren't good enough.

"When I let go of all that I am, I become all that I might be."

~ Lao Tzu

I was never able to heal my own eating disorders by looking at them directly. I couldn't fix the bulimia by identifying as a bulimic. But I could fix the self-loathing and the feeling of being trapped in a body. I could discover that I loved myself, and that I was more soul than body, this temporary human vehicle. As I cultivated a spiritual practice and used Kundalini Yoga to restore the energetic flow of life force within my body, I found that things healed on their own. Gradually, and in stages, the tools in this book stopped my self-destructive behaviors in their tracks. When I identified as Spirit, the natural flow of well-being was slowly restored to my body and mind. When I stopped treating myself like a crazy girl and started treating myself like a divine Spirit living on Earth as a woman, I connected with a power so great and infinite that my problems shrank before it. Loving my reflection, feeling beautiful from the inside out, and radically accepting myself no matter what the number read on the scale became things I could do—and you can, too.

If you've never had a strong sense of spirituality, some of this might feel a little out there. But humor me and suspend your disbelief long enough to give this a try. After all, hating yourself will take everything from you, so there will be nothing left to lose. In loving yourself, you stand to gain everything.

To really use this program successfully, let go of statements like "I am a bulimic, I am too fat, I am ugly" that run around in your head. Let go of all the "I am" statements that you have ever known. Let your "I am" be replaced by an ***I Am*** with greater potential and power than you ever knew you had. Allow your ***I Am*** to be revealed to you in the depths of meditation, where you can feel your soul, which is pure love.

I called this book ***The Body Temple*** because healing from the cycle of self-loathing required that I stop relating to myself as a body, and instead see my body as a temple. I had to relate to myself as something holy, precious, and worth adoration. Every time I take a bath or get dressed or brush my hair or do yoga or eat a meal, I have the opportunity to worship at the altar of my Body Temple. Every time I take a deep breath, I have the chance to honor myself and cleanse my temple. Each time I say "I love you" or chant a mantra to myself, it's like lighting a candle within. After hundreds, even thousands, of times, my temple is now filled with a beautiful, angelic glow. I now recognize that my spirit is that Light, and my soul is much more at home within this physical form than ever before. Harmony between body, mind, and spirit creates a deep and precious peace within.

Knowing that there is a power greater than me made me humble; realizing that I could connect with this power and tap into it made me strong. That power belongs to you, too. That power of self-awareness is the Kundalini, and in this book are tools for awakening it and transforming your life.

I see beauty within me and all around me.

CHAPTER 3

On Body Image and Eating Disorders

"If I asked you to name all the things that you love, how long would it take you to name yourself?"

~ Unknown

Lack of self-love and self-acceptance is a global epidemic. But somehow, if you are reading this book, I don't think I need to convince you of that. I think you feel it in your heart. Simply imagine how much energy you would free up if instead of depleting yourself with self-harm and self-ridicule, you lifted yourself up with self-care. Imagine how much mental space you would free up if you didn't fill your mind with thoughts about your weight. Imagine how good it would feel to love yourself no matter the number on the scale.

This isn't a book about eating disorders; this is a book about learning to love yourself. It's here to give you the tools you need to support your journey to recovery. There are millions of people suffering with eating disorders, whether they are anorexic, bulimic, compulsive overeaters, or another variation on self-loathing. Eating disorders are among the most dangerous mental health problems and many people never recover, dying from their disease. You can read other books to find out more about eating disorders and how they affect society. I'm not writing this book to teach you about eating disorders. This book is about you and the journey home to your soul. In fact, I don't think you should identify as anything but a soul with a body and a being of light.

"First love your body, then love your mind, and then love your soul, and then love your totality, then love your reality. These five things you must do."

~ Yogi Bhajan, June 4, 1992

My hope is that this book helps you learn to fall madly in love with yourself. I don't meet people who are suffering from an eating disorder and think, "Oh that's an anorexic." I think, "That's a person who needs support." This book is about the transformational potential of Kundalini Yoga as taught by Yogi Bhajan® and its power to help you learn to love yourself again. You can't be madly in love with yourself and have an eating disorder. You also can't be madly in love with yourself and not love your body. My own journey through eating disorders and the practice of Kundalini Yoga has given me that. I don't always wake up every day falling over myself with love, but when I do my practice, when I meditate and reconnect, my soul bubbles up on its own and keeps me healthy, happy, and safe.

Yogi Bhajan, the Master of Kundalini Yoga who brought it to the West from India, never gave lectures about eating disorders. He rarely mentioned anorexia or bulimia and didn't give any specific kriyas or meditations for them. He didn't specifically treat disease with his teachings. For him, the thousands of kriyas and meditations that he shared were for everyone. They were for connecting with Spirit and allowing your well-being to flow through you. He did give a couple of techniques for conscious eating, *Pranayama for Compulsive Overeating* and *Bhoj Kriya*, which I share later in this book, but they were primarily to teach people about the havoc they wreak on their system by consuming too much food. He believed that loving your body was crucially important for the health of your spirit; in the quote above, he put loving your body as the first step, the critically important foundational step to building a life of balance: mind, soul, and body.

For this book, I have used my knowledge as a teacher of Kundalini Yoga and my intuition as a survivor of eating disorders to put into your hands a combination of the tools I have used to learn to love myself, and the tools I wish I had known about when I was at my worst. But in truth, after you do heal and come home to your heart, you can continue to use this practice to uplift yourself and keep yourself healthy; in fact, it is the only way I've found to stay healthy.

Love your scars.
Love your wounds.
Love all of yourself.
Every tiny bit.

Kundalini Yoga is for everyone, all the time. You definitely don't have to have an eating disorder to benefit from the tools found here. In fact, this book is more about being body positive than anything else. To come into divine alignment and allow that positivity, toward yourself and your body, to heal anything that is out of alignment within you, is my hope for everyone. A little extra self-love and self-care never hurts, so please, share this with the people you wish loved themselves as much as you love them.

LOW-SELF ESTEEM AND POOR BODY IMAGE

You don't have to have an eating disorder to have disordered eating. You can have a healthy relationship to food and still have an unhealthy image of your own body. Maybe if you slip up on your diet and eat a cookie, your day feels ruined. Maybe if you come back from vacation and you've put on a few pounds, you feel terrible about yourself. Maybe when you look in the mirror you think that if only you lost 10 pounds, then you could feel good about yourself and start accomplishing your dreams. Maybe your mood is directly tied to whether or not you're having a "skinny jeans day."

"You are the beauty. You don't need the beauty."

~ Yogi Bhajan, July 26, 1996

Your ability to create the life of your dreams is directly tied to your emotional and psychological projection. If your energy is tied up in moodiness because of imagined physical deficits and mental preoccupations, you'll never have the energy to project positively and manifest what it is you want.

Low self-esteem is sometimes something we are born with. Loss of self-esteem can happen in utero, even at the moment of conception. Many spiritual paths believe that if either of your parents were out of harmony or depressed during your conception or pregnancy, you could have been born with naturally low self-esteem. Early childhood traumas, or use of narcotics or alcohol, can also affect self-esteem and body acceptance. It is absolutely possible through Kundalini Yoga to rehabilitate the body and mind from the effects of these traumas and toxins, and recreate our personality to project positivity and self-confidence.

You're going to need to be honest with yourself. If you are struggling with low self-esteem, what you are really doing is burying your light. Why are you afraid to shine? If you are constantly criticizing your body, whose voice are you speaking with? Picking yourself apart doesn't serve your light; nor does living a life where you cripple your talents and abilities by living in a shadow.

You are not your body. I'm going to say this again: *You are not your body*. You are a spirit that has incarnated into a body. And your body is in love with your spirit. Without your soul, your body is nothing but carbon and dust. Your soul animates every cell, and gives life and meaning and purpose to every molecule of who you are. It does nothing but support you and honor you. It's about time you began to treat it with the same respect. It deserves love, and so do you. So if you have a negative body image, declare a truce. Extend a hand to yourself and begin a new journey into kindness, compassion, and generosity. If you need to lose weight, then fine, allow yourself to let go of what no longer serves you, but stop punishing something that is innocent and good. You are pure and good and worthy. You may need to read that a hundred times before you believe it. But opening yourself up to that truth is the first step into a very new, very beautiful life.

You are pure and good and worthy.

CHANGING BODIES, CHANGING BODY IMAGE

Many people find that they gain weight at some point in their lives, often significant amounts. Everyone has a reason: an injury, the birth of a child, the loss of a loved one, a health challenge, a stressful job, the natural aging process. Maybe one day you wake up and realize over the last decade you've put on 100 pounds. If you look in the mirror and don't like what you see, how do you still like you?

Body acceptance doesn't mean you never want to change anything about your body ever again. It doesn't mean that you can't motivate yourself towards losing weight in a healthy, balanced way when appropriate. In fact, if you have weight to lose, doing kriya and meditation can balance your hormones and adrenal glands, shift your metabolism, and assist in the journey, but I would much rather you focus on losing the weight in your heart rather than the weight on your body. Body acceptance means that you love yourself at any weight, in any shape, in the here and now without any changes at all. Lead with love; making changes for health and fitness that support your goals, while loving yourself every step of the way, is the key.

> "If a mirror ever makes you sad: know that it cannot know you."
>
>  Kabir

If you find that your body has changed to the point that it is unrecognizable to you, that you feel like you are trapped in a cage, or walking around in someone else's skin, relief from those feelings is critical. Learning to reconnect with your spirit will allow your soul to feel free again. Loving yourself when you don't look the way you would like is a challenge. Self-love is a muscle, and you will find that the more you are challenged into loving yourself, the stronger the bond of love you are able to build. You have to remember that the number on a scale tells you absolutely nothing important about who you are. It cannot and will not ever be able to measure your *Sat Nam*, your True Identity.

By putting into place the mantras, kriyas, meditations, and guided visualizations in this book, you can learn to be comfortable in whatever skin you are in. Beauty is in the eye of the beholder, but the only beholder that matters is you. You are beautiful right now, just as you are, before you even begin. You don't need to apologize for your shape. You don't need to hide yourself in the back of a yoga class. You are beautiful no matter what size pants you have on. The practices in this book will simply give you the eyes to see.

UNDERSTANDING THE ENERGETIC EFFECTS OF EATING DISORDERS

"When you do not consciously relate to your body, your mind does not relate consciously to you."

~ Yogi Bhajan, January 30, 1985

Eating disorders cause immense physical, psychological, and spiritual damage. They have some of the highest mortality rates of all mental disorders. Even a single negative thought diminishes your aura, so you can imagine what repeatedly abusing your mind and body with self-loathing thoughts and actions do to it. You can't live up to your fullest potential because living with poor self-esteem ties both hands behind your back and then asks you to perform brain surgery.

Healing from your eating disorder is more than a fight for your life; it is a fight for your sanity, for your spirit, and for your right to exist in peace, grace, and radiance in this world.

Eating Disorders and Their Impact in the United States

Eating disorders have the highest mortality rate of any mental illness[1]; in the United States alone, where up to 30 million people are believed to have an eating disorder[2] such as bulimia, anorexia, or binge eating, this is a critical problem. Women in particular are hit hard by an epidemic of cultural expectation on physical beauty and perfection that often leaves them feeling like they aren't good enough; young women are hit the hardest, though this damage may stay with them throughout their lives. Women between the ages of 12 and 26 make up to 95% of people with eating disorders[3], and 25% of college women have turned to bingeing and purging as a weight loss technique[4]. Studies have found that up to 50% of teenage girls and 25% of teenage boys have participated in unhealthy weight control behaviors such as fasting, vomiting, or laxatives[5]. Yet even though this is widespread, the stigma around eating disorders is still so strong that only 1 in 10 people who are suffering receive treatment[6].

Depression and Low Self-Esteem

Many people who suffer from eating disorders, low body acceptance, and a lack of self-love also experience depression and other mental health problems. The stigma of depression and mental health challenges often keep people reaching out for support. According to the National Institute of Diabetes and Digestive and Kidney Diseases, as many as half of the people with Binge Eating Disorder also suffer from depression. Additionally, a 2008 study at the University of Pittsburgh Medical Center showed that 24% of bipolar patients met the criteria for eating disorders[6b].

Depression and low self-esteem don't always lead to an eating disorder, but it is worth addressing the connection between feeling depressed and not feeling comfortable in your body. It is always worth trying new techniques to come into a greater sense of self-appreciation and self-care. You will find many tools in this book to manage your own depression or to share with people you think may be suffering from a dark night of the soul.

Eating Disorders and Our Children

It's also clear that we need to do better to teach our children to love and honor their Body Temples. An article in the Journal of Adolescent Health reported that 81% of 10-year-olds are afraid of being fat[7]. Children's minds should be filled with play, laughter, and discovering what excites them in this world, not worried about what their bodies look like or how they perform, and they certainly shouldn't be subject to insult or bullying based on their weight. If you are the parent of a child who is suffering from disordered eating, secretive food behaviors, or an obsession with their looks and weight, please seek professional help for them. Watch your words about your own body and self-esteem. Begin introducing your children to yoga and meditation, opening up a way for them to dialogue with their spirits and find peaceful ways to resolve stress and develop self-worth.

We have to change this on a generational level; we have to teach self-love from the very first breath. If we want this to change for our children and grandchildren, we must change it within ourselves and we must change it now. Try sharing some of the simpler meditations in this book with them, a few minutes at a time. Don't expect perfect posture or perfect pronunciation. For younger children, make yoga a game and use language appropriate to their age. Teenagers can dive right in at the adult level. It's time to change the paradigm.

If you have a young child that is showing signs of body consciousness or low self-esteem, try this meditation with them:

"I Am Happy" Meditation for Children

If children are in an environment where their parents are fighting, conflict can be absorbed into their delicate psyches and manifest in a variety of unhealthy ways down the line. This meditation was originally given for children to use when their parents are fighting to remain unaffected by the energy but it can be done any time, including when the child needs a boost of body-positive, confidence-boosting fun!

Sit in Easy Pose. Make fists of your hands and point your index fingers straight up. Shake your fingers in time with the rhythm of the mantra, bringing them from pointing straight up and down to pointing at a 30-degree angle (like wagging your finger "NO!").

Sing the words: *"I am Happy, I am Good. I am Happy, I am Good. Sat Nam Sat Nam Sat Nam Ji. Waheguru Waheguru Waheguru Ji."* This mantra connects you to your inner truth and happiness. Continue as long as the child has fun!

Eating Disorders and Men

Males make up 10-15% of those with eating disorders[8], and they are less likely to reach out for treatment because society considers eating disorders a "woman's thing[9]." Let me be clear here: men are welcome. This book is for everyone, male, female, transgender, non-binary; all deserve the healing power of self-love and the transformational technology of Kundalini Yoga, and everyone deserves to feel included in such an important conversation.

BULIMIA

From a clinical perspective, *Bulimia Nervosa* is a serious, potentially life-threatening disorder marked by a cycle of bingeing and purging. According to the National Institute of Mental Health, it affects up to 4.2% of women[10]. Bulimics often realize that their behaviors are unhealthy and dangerous, but continue compulsively. What bulimics may not realize is that their behaviors can be lethal; a study in the American Journal of Psychiatry put the mortality rate for bulimics at 3.9%[11]. Unlike those with anorexia, bulimics tend to be of normal weight, so it's more difficult to spot, but the health effects can include tooth decay, gastric or esophageal rupture, electrolyte imbalance, heart problems, and chronic irregular bowel movements.

Purging may be through self-induced vomiting, over-exercising, or abusing laxatives and diuretics. Those experiencing bulimia tend to have their self-esteem entirely tied up in their body image. The feeling of being out of control is common, especially during active binge/purge cycles. The need to exercise or "burn off" the calories consumed during a binge can also become an obsession.

From a human perspective, bulimia isn't so simple to nail down. Some people start bingeing and purging from a very young age as a way of dieting, but for others it is more of an unhealthy stress reliever. For me, it began as a way of managing stress and transformed into a serious addiction. I didn't have better tools as a young woman to deal with the combination of being a serious overachiever who demanded perfection from herself in school and being an intuitive empath who could feel the emotions and energies of those around her. Without healthy ways to process those internal demands, like kriya and meditation, I turned to bulimia as a way of dealing with the world.

Like so many young women, I also fell victim to societal standards of airbrushed beauty and believed that I had to strive to achieve an ideal that very few people naturally embody. As I reached puberty and the push to be "attractive" hit, my behaviors accelerated and bulimia became a way of dieting. The reason I share this inside look into bulimia is because if you are attempting to help a bulimic recover, it's important to know that it's not all about weight. It's a compulsive reaction to excessive stress and self-loathing that turns into being about weight and body image. It can start as one thing and morph into another. If you hate yourself, bulimia can be a way of punishing yourself. It can be about food, but it doesn't have to be. It doesn't matter whether someone is bulimic because they are compulsively dieting or mentally ill. From my perspective, bulimia is a violent separation between the body and spirit. To relieve this disorder, you must reconnect with your spirit. You must allow the body and spirit to make peace, to coexist in light and love, and to deeply love and accept yourself for who you are.

Yoga Tip for Bulimics:
Excessive amounts of purging wreaks havoc on the teeth. The harsh acids of the stomach are too much for the delicate enamel of our teeth. If you have a history of purging, try oil pulling, an ancient Ayurvedic treatment for tooth and gum disease.

How to Oil Pull:
Place about one tablespoon sesame oil, preferably organic (you can use coconut or other oils if preferred), into your mouth and swish the oil around for 20 minutes. Don't swish so hard that your cheeks become sore. Do NOT swallow the oil, but spit it out at the end. It will pull toxins out of hard-to-reach spaces in your mouth. Brush normally after oil pulling. This is a wonderful tool to encourage dental health naturally.

Recovery happens in stages. Learning not to beat yourself up when you slip is huge. In Kundalini Yoga, traditionally meditations are done for 40 consecutive days; if you miss a day, you start over at day 1. For me, this was a critical teaching to absorb. Let your recovery be a meditation. If you start a journey to healing and you binge and purge one day, your journey does not have to be over. Just start again. You shoot for 40 days with no bingeing and purging, then you shoot for 90 days, then 120 days, then 1,000 days. Mark your days off on a calendar to keep track. If you mess up one day, you start at day 1, but you keep up and you keep going. Eventually you live your way into a life without bingeing and purging, into a life without self-harm, one day at a time. Drench yourself in love, and sweetly and softly live your way into a richer life.

ANOREXIA

From a clinical perspective, *Anorexia Nervosa* is a serious, life-threatening disorder that is characterized by self-starvation and extreme weight loss. According to the Renfrew Center for Eating Disorders, between 1-4.2% of all American women experience anorexia. It has one of the highest death rates for any mental illness; 20% of people with anorexia will prematurely die from complications[12].

Anorexia is characterized by starvation of the body and a preoccupation with weight loss; as a consequence, this behavior starves the body of essential nutrients and slows down many essential functions of the body, causing damage to many systems. Physical complications from anorexia may include low heart rate and blood pressure, bone loss, heart damage, muscle loss, dehydration, kidney failure, exhaustion, and hair loss. There is nothing about anorexia that is good for the body.

Anorexics tend to have a tremendous preoccupation with weight loss; an inability to see themselves as anything other than "too fat"; secretive food rituals, including hiding food; and general depression.

From a human perspective, anorexics withdraw from food and from life. Anorexia is a disease of self-annihilation. The obsession with weight loss becomes the defining characteristic of each day.

Anorexia is a denial of self-love. Food is one of the most nourishing things we give our bodies. Denying our body that nourishment is a spiritual crisis where we withhold not only nourishment but also love and connection. Anorexia relates to being uncomfortable in the physical world, not feeling safe, worthy, or grounded. The obsession with being thin even to the point of death is an assertion that death is safer than living. The mind imprints this as "thin is safe and fat is dangerous." By eliminating food, one begins to feel more immaterial. But there is no escape from physicality and so the body feels no relief. The carrot continues to move, and no matter how underweight a person becomes, they still think they have more weight to lose and that once they lose it they will feel better.

My experience with anorexia grew out of a healthy desire to make a positive change in my life. After years of bulimia and compulsive overeating, I wanted to get healthy before I went off to college. So I began an eating and exercise program that resulted in weight loss. However, because I had never dealt with my underlying self-esteem issues, when people began to compliment me on my weight loss, their external validation led to a compulsive desire to continue to be "worthy" of acclaim, which translated as losing more weight. I restricted my food intake, my fat gram intake, obsessively counted calories, and began to work out about 4 hours a day. I became very thin, started to experience pain when sitting because of fat loss, and I was constantly cold. However, when I got to college, my stress levels went up and my previous addiction to bulimia, which had developed as a way of managing stress, re-emerged as my dominant trait, and my weight returned to more normal levels. I remember feeling that the most value I had was in my body, never mind that I was a smart woman going to college, or that I could contribute to the world. It felt like I was asleep to everything but how I looked on the outside.

If I could go back in time and talk to the girl I was then, I would talk about having to have another point on the graph other than my body. My weight, my body, how I looked, none of these things related to my talents, my intelligence, or my dreams. From a yogic perspective, anorexia is being trapped in the illusion of maya, on one hand valuing yourself based only on the illusion of your body, which has become distorted, and on the other being so terrified that there is nothing beyond the illusion that you forget to live.

Moving beyond anorexia requires that you make peace with living in this world, that you address your fears and anxieties, that you balance your chakras, repair your body system by system, and reconnect to your spirit so that you might find dreams beyond the scale.

It can be a difficult journey, but it can also save your life.

BINGE EATING DISORDER

Clinically, Binge Eating Disorder (BED) is characterized by consuming an inordinately large quantity of food in a limited period of time (approximately 2 hours). During the episode, one feels out of control and unable to stop eating. There are many aspects of overeating that can be used to characterize this condition: eating when not full, eating extremely large quantities, eating to a point of discomfort and feeling guilty or depressed when finished. Many people experience overeating and can benefit from treating their behaviors, but to have Binge Eating Disorder, you must engage in these behaviors at least once a week for over 3 months. People with BED generally do not engage in purging, as in bulimia, and so are confronted with different health challenges as a result of their addiction.

Binge Eating Disorder can cause excessive weight gain, which can lead to aching joints, diabetes, high blood pressure, gallbladder problems, heart disease, and morbid obesity. It is important to note that not everyone who is overweight or obese has BED, and not everyone with BED is obese.

From a human perspective, many things can trigger the start of Binge Eating Disorder. Usually it's emotions: anger, anxiety, shame, depression. All of these uncomfortable emotions can trigger the urge to eat until the feeling of being full pushes those emotions away. Whether you have compulsive overeating behaviors or just one night of eating a gallon of ice cream on the couch, overeating comes from trying to numb negative feelings and cut yourself off from the source of spirit. People who tend toward this type of eating feel a lot of shame because their behavior is out of control, but it is exactly these types who are controlling, perfectionist, and highly achieving individuals who care about what other people think about them.

Many people with BED, or those compulsive overeaters who are at risk of developing it, have experienced shame about their bodies, usually in the form of being teased as a child or adolescent for being overweight. Pain from these episodes can become lodged in both the subconscious and conscious minds and create false beliefs and negative behavioral patterns. I remember being bullied mercilessly in middle school and high school for being overweight. I had been put on lifesaving medication that made me gain 60 pounds in fourth grade. I was called "ugly," "fat," "gross"—you name it—and it took a long time for those scars to heal because those years are so formative and our auras are so sensitive. Taking the time to forgive the children in my memories for their words has released me from needing to carry forward any trigger from those experiences. Forgiveness of ourselves and others is the key to healing.

The shame of overeating has to stop. Most of the people who experience this condition will not admit it. Fear of being judged is a huge barrier to truth-telling, especially in the yoga and spiritual communities. But binge eating is a challenging addiction to overcome. When you are addicted to alcohol, you can stop drinking, but when your addiction is overeating, you cannot stop eating altogether.

In yogic philosophy, compulsive overeating relates to an imbalance in the hemispheres of the brain. Yogi Bhajan said, "Compulsive eating, irrational eating, and uncontrolled eating are self-depriving factors in the eastern hemisphere of the brain[13]." In my personal opinion, one of the best ways to address long-term bingeing behaviors is to use pranayam, or breathing exercises, to calm and balance the brain. You will find meditations in this book to support this. But whether you have Binge Eating Disorder, or you just tend to overeat, use your breath to reconnect to your body, to drop into your Self, and feel what it's like to exist, to be human. You have to become comfortable with being alive. You can't keep stuffing life away, pushing your emotions and your spirit further away. You have to take a deep breath, make peace with existing in human form, fill yourself with an awareness of spirit, and exhale a deep feeling of self-love. And then you have to do that again and again and again.

There is nothing shameful about you. There is nothing shameful about your body. There is nothing shameful about your eating. You are beautiful, just as you are. If you do have Binge Eating Disorder or struggle with compulsive overeating, imagine how much better you would feel if your stomach stopped hurting, if you felt vital and alive in your body, and if you felt good about yourself every day. Allow your healing to be joyful and fun, one breath at a time.

ORTHOREXIA

Orthorexia is not currently recognized as a clinical disorder, but I include it here because it plagues the yoga and other spiritual communities and deserves some attention and light shed upon it.

Orthorexia was coined by Steven Bratman, MD[14] to describe certain patients who took healthy eating to unhealthy extremes. Healthy eating is not unhealthy, but orthorexia is when someone becomes obsessively fixated on the purity of the food they are eating to an extreme. They can become completely consumed with how much or how little to eat, the source of their foods, the handling of their foods. It can potentially become physically dangerous when someone ignores their body's own health needs in order to pursue an ideal eating regimen.

Orthorexia is not like other eating disorders in that people do not tend to fixate on weight loss or purging but instead on an extreme ideal of health. At the point that this interest in health turns into something that prevents someone from enjoying time with friends and family, impedes other activities, or causes someone to ignore physical warning signs, it becomes an issue. Not everyone who eats a restricted, health-conscious diet is orthorexic; for example, a vegan is not an orthorexic. But someone who refuses to eat for three days because no organic food is available may be.

A doctor may not diagnose orthorexia because it is not in the DSM-5 diagnostic manual, but if you are concerned that your healthy diet has gone too far, it's still important to reach out to a medical professional. You might think that sounds silly, but for me, I followed a very strict and idealistic diet for two years. I began suffering from pain in my joints and fatigue, but would not relax my "perfect" diet and ignored the problems until they severely limited my ability to function. I later discovered that I was extremely deficient in Vitamin D. I had thought my diet was healthy, but it lacked an essential vitamin. I had to adjust my philosophical ideals to give my body what it needed to be healthy.

Orthorexia is about being inflexible and becoming rigid with yourself and the world around you. Dharma can easily become dogma if your ego asserts itself and convinces you that anyone is above or below another. Moving your spine can help your mind become more flexible. Combining an active kriya practice with self-love meditations and healing mantras can help you release your attachment to a rigid protocol when it no longer serves you, while still maintaining a healthy diet and lifestyle.

BODY DYSMORPHIA DISORDER

Body Dysmorphia Disorder (BDD) isn't an eating disorder, but an anxiety disorder that affects self-image and is found in about 1.2-2.4% of the population[15].*

Most people have something they don't like about their bodies. Maybe you don't like your thighs, your nose, or your teeth. But people with Body Dysmorphia Disorder are filled with an obsession about their imperfections, whether real or imagined. They spend hours each day thinking about their physical flaws. They have a difficult time controlling negative thinking and rarely believe others who they tell them they look fine. They often resort to obsessive skin picking, a way of trying to pick out their imperfections.

I personally believe that a key to overcoming a severe disorder in self-perception is to learn to control the mind. You can do so through meditations for the Negative Mind and negative thoughts. It is also helpful to address issues of perfectionism and balancing the brain through meditation.

I have never personally experienced Body Dysmorphic Disorder, but I do know what it's like to hate your body. I know that when I was a size 6, I felt fatter than when I was a size 16. I know what it's like to spend hours of your life every day thinking about how you look and obsessing over external appearance. It's draining, exhausting, and wastes much of your creative vitality.

If you are experiencing obsessive thoughts about your flaws, it is time to re-balance your Positive and Negative Minds, to reconnect with your ability to love yourself, and to reconnect with yourself as a spirit rather than the body. When you allow your ego to dominate, you are identifying with your ego self rather than your higher Self; but your True Self, your *Sat Nam*, is where your greatest

---

* Body Dysmorphia Disorder should not be confused with Gender Dysphoria, which is a state of feeling a mismatch between ones' gender identity and biological sex. Many transgendered people are misdiagnosed as having Body Dysmorphia Disorder. (Source: Callahan, Kate. *Stop Confusing Gender Dysphoria with Body Dysmorphia Already. ROYGBIV.* August 2014.)

well-being lies. Your greatest destiny is not physical perfection. You have come here to give a gift to the world. If you are struggling with BDD or a severely poor self-image, follow the kriyas and meditations in this book to learn to control your negative thinking in order to give you the greatest chance for a positive life.

LETTING GO OF LABELS

If you do have an eating disorder, at this point in the book I'd like to ask you to drop your self-identification with the label. The "I am" statement is one of the most powerful things we can speak into creation. You must come to terms with having a problem in order to fix it, but once you have identified and accepted that you need help, I encourage you to create space in your life to be more than your problems.

You are not your challenges; your challenges are what you are called to overcome.

Watch your self-talk. If you have bulimia, don't say "I am a bulimic." Say "I have bulimia" instead. That turns it from who you are to what you have, and you can release what you have. The only truth about who you are is your *Sat Nam*, your True Identity, which is perfection. What you truly are is radiant grace and divine love and intelligence. You may be experiencing an eating disorder, or you may have low self-esteem, but you are much more than those limited experiences. You are not your challenges; your challenges are what you are called to overcome.

To begin a journey into self-healing, to overcome the challenges you face, you must release your story and go into Truth. You are light, you are love, you are peace.

Go to spiritvoyage.com/bodytemple for guided meditations that I've designed specifically to support your eating disorder, food addiction, and self-worth recovery and healing journey.

THE SPIRAL PATH

The path to recovery is often not a straight line, but a spiral. As you start to heal, you may get frustrated when you relapse. When I was in the process of healing, I would get so angry with myself when I would find myself engaging in unhealthy behaviors. But from the vantage point of time and gentleness, I realize that my recovery was a spiral path. Learning self-love, self-forgiveness, and body acceptance is one of the great lessons of my life. The spiral path allowed me to return to this core teaching again and again, learning the lesson more deeply on each return, until at last I was far enough away from the epicenter of pain that I left its orbit. Don't get frustrated with yourself when you don't live up to an ideal; you may find that with your own time and gentleness, your spiral path was perfect, too.

I deeply love and accept myself.

CHAPTER 4

Kundalini Yoga

"Kundalini Yoga will give you Grace at the weakest point of your life."

~ Yogi Bhajan

ABOUT KUNDALINI YOGA AS TAUGHT BY YOGI BHAJAN®

Kundalini Yoga was first brought to the attention of the West in the late 1960s by Yogi Bhajan. It is a technology to awaken your consciousness. As you practice Kundalini Yoga, you grow; you shed old behaviors, attitudes, and self-destructive habits, gaining new perspectives, capacities, and habits that support your own continued evolution.

Kundalini Yoga is a complete system of yoga. It is known as the Yoga of Awareness, and its goal is to assist you into coming into a state of greater awareness and enlightenment. To paraphrase Yogi Bhajan, when you recognize your own inner light, you become enlightened. It incorporates many aspects of yoga: asana, mudra, pranayam, mantra, seva, kriya, meditation, and more. In this book, we will primarily deal with kriya and meditation, which incorporate asana (posture), pranayam (breathing), mudra (hand positions), bandha (body locks), and mantra (words)[16].

If you find yourself getting overwhelmed by any of these concepts, especially if they are brand new to you, just skip them! You don't need to understand any of the yogic principles for the kriyas, mantras, and meditations in this book to work. This information is just that, information; the real juice lies in the practice.

KRIYA

Never change a kriya; instead let the kriya change you.

A kriya is an action that leads to manifestation. Just like a sunflower seed blooms into a sunflower and an iris bulb blooms into an iris, a kriya is made up of a codified sequence of postures, pranayam, and mantras that flow together in a specific energetic way for specific, repeatable results. When you focus on a particular kriya and practice it, the energy within your body responds by moving in a very precise way. Kriyas can look similar or different, and there are thousands within the lexicon of Kundalini Yoga as taught by Yogi Bhajan®. Never change a kriya; instead let the kriya change you. If it is difficult for you, stick with it. There are rewards for every challenge.

Asana

In any kriya or meditation, you may be asked to get into a particular posture, or asana. In a kriya, an asana can be used to isolate specific muscles and put pressure on particular meridian points. It may also serve to increase circulation or move lymph[17]. In a meditation, posture creates the foundation for the practice. Each asana impacts a specific location in the body where blocks and triggers may be removed. An asana provides a pathway for prana (life-force energy) to circulate throughout the body.

Keep the teachings exactly as they are with the exception of reducing the times of the postures. When you first begin an asana, you might feel awkward if you've never done it before. Settle into it and allow the muscles you aren't using to relax. Allow yourself to become aware of the muscles you are using. Release into the posture and in that simple act of letting go, you will establish an important connection to yourself.

Kundalini Yoga is a geometry of the human body and the fulfillment of the human psyche[18]. Every angle and triangle that is created within your body through asana has an effect. For example, lifting your legs to 30 degrees influences your Navel Point. If you lift your arms to 60 degrees, your heart and lungs get the benefit. Extend your arms out to the sides, and you are engaging your heart meridian and uprooting deep-seated emotions. Essentially your entire body is a geometric grid. If the triangles in the body are not evenly aligned, it will result in an energy imbalance, just as a poorly drawn triangle wouldn't translate to good structural integrity in an architectural blueprint. A good visualization game to play is to sit in Easy Pose and tune in to your body. Where can you find your hidden triangles? What parts of your body connect and relate in a geometric way? Many people explore sacred geometry in the outer world. I invite you to explore it in your inner world. Your body really is an incredible miracle; tune in to your own body and discover your own sacred geometry as a way of relating to your physical form in a non-critical, exploratory way.

Meditation

Meditation trains and focuses the mind, while calming physical body systems. It is the most powerful lifestyle tool I know for growth and self-empowerment. There are many styles of meditation; some involve mantra and some are silent. Some have motions and some are completely motionless. Experiment with the meditations in this book either by doing them all one at a time, or finding one that resonates with you and continuing it for 40, 90, 120, or 1,000 days.

Meditations often involve drishti, mudra, bandha, or pranayam. Don't worry! If these words make yoga feel intimidating, just ignore them. We could just as easily have said meditations often involve eye focus, hand position, body locks, or breathing exercises. Using the original Sanskrit is perhaps more correct to the tradition, but the tradition should never intimidate anyone into shying away from the experience.

Drishti

Drishti, or the science of eye focus, means pure seeing. Drishti is to the eyes what asana is to the body. Correct drishti helps keep the body in the correct posture and the mind focused on the task at hand. Eye focus directs prana in the body. Correct drishti is important, so when you are reading your Kundalini Yoga kriya, take care to follow the eye focus instructions.

In Kundalini Yoga, eyes are most often shut, but when an eye focus is specified, it has a particular energetic effect on the kriya or meditation. Eye focus can be done with eyes closed or open, so make sure to closely follow instructions. Beginners often make the mistake of trying to force an eye focus, but correct drishti never involves straining the eyes. If you are called upon to focus on the tip of the nose and this hurts your eyes, more practice is required for the muscles around the eyes to get into perfect placement. To work up to this, simply relax the gaze slightly and meet yourself and your muscles where you are. Increase the strength of your gaze as your practice deepens.

Brow Point. Also called the Third Eye, this gaze stimulates the pituitary gland, strengthening intuition. It also affects the sushmuna, which is the central column along the spine through which prana flows. Consciously moving energy through the sushmuna builds up your aura.

Tip of the Nose. Formally known as Agiaa Chakra Bandh, or Lotus Drishti, in addition to being a drishti, this focus is a body lock. Locks are like complex dam systems that direct the flow of energy throughout the body in very specific ways. It stimulates the pineal gland and the frontal lobe of the brain, creating new pathways in the brain. It can be very challenging for beginners, as there is pressure placed on the optic nerve.

Chin. This is the Moon Center gaze, and like the energy of the moon, it brings cooling and calming energy. It is very reflective, allowing introspection.

Crown Chakra. Focusing the gaze on the Crown Chakra, or 10th gate, stimulates it to open. It also affects the pineal gland.

$1/10^{th}$ Open. Also sometimes written as $9/10^{th}$ Closed, in this drishti, your eyes are relaxed and unfocused. This gaze is balancing and calming, and it develops intuition. It allows your entire system to remain open to the effects of the meditation.

Mudra

A mudra is a hand position that guides energy flow in a particular way. By utilizing hand positions, we can affect many systems in the body and emotional responses. When holding a mudra, the pressure should be consistent and firm but not rigid or taxing. It is also worth noting that a mudra is done with the fleshy part of the finger (not the fingernail) unless specified.

Some common mudras:

- **Gyan Mudra:** forefinger and thumb touch, for wisdom and receptivity
- **Shuni Mudra:** middle finger and thumb touch, for patience and commitment
- **Ravi Mudra:** ring finger and thumb touch, for energy and good health

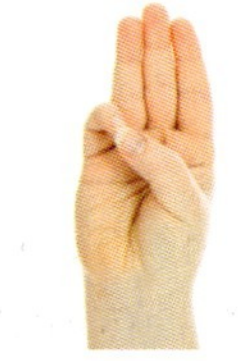

- **Buddhi Mudra:** pinkie and thumb touch, for intuition and good communication

- **Prayer Pose:** Palms together at chest, for centering and being neutral

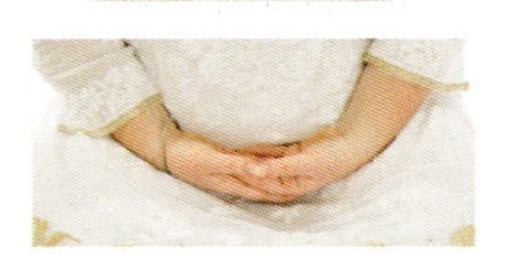

- **Buddha Mudra:** hands in the lap, for meditativeness

You can practice mudras at any time, even separately from meditation and kriya. The next time you are bored, say waiting for an appointment, put your hands in a mudra and allow energy to circulate through your body in a healthy, healing way. You might even decide to mentally recite a mantra to go with it. This will give your mind something to do other than obsess about your weight while you wait, and will retrain your mind to default to more positive thoughts that don't self-sabotage you any time you are bored or restless.

Pranayam

We all breathe. If we don't, we die. That's pretty simple. And yet, breathing is much more than just that. Pattern, frequency, depth; all of these contribute to our body's biorhythms. We aren't conscious of breathing most of the time, and therein lies the difference between breathing and pranayam. Pranayam is the science of breathing consciously, controlling the movement of prana (life force) through the use of specific techniques. Breathing gives us life; pranayam gives us quality of life.

Many people have learned to breathe incorrectly, and therefore inhale by drawing the belly in. This actually makes less space for air in the lungs rather than more. Proper, normal breathing patterns are as follows: when you breathe in, your navel moves out; when you breathe out, your navel moves in. Use the nose to filter the air as you inhale and exhale completely. If you are breathing incorrectly, or paradoxically, take the time to retrain yourself and practice breathing correctly. You'll see the benefits as you learn proper stress management and work to clear and release emotional states.

Another common breathing mistake is shallow, erratic breathing in the upper chest. If you are not engaging your navel with your breath, you are not breathing deeply enough. Proper breathing changes the amount of energy you have in reserve to manage emergencies. It is also a direct path to the development of higher consciousness. Shallow breathing is caused by stress and over long periods of time tends to weaken our nervous system, creating an environment ripe for illness. Without proper breathing patterns, trauma, which is stored in our muscular system, can't release. Deep breathing allows us to drop the body armor we build up to shield ourselves from trauma, which left alone stiffens both the body and the heart. Correct breathing increases the flow of prana, so you feel increased vitality and a general sense of well-being.

A note of caution: if you feel dizzy while doing pranayam during any of the kriyas or meditations in this book, stop. Go back to normal breathing until you feel better. Lung capacity and nervous system strength are built through consistency, not through force.

Throughout this book, in meditations and kriyas, I mention Long Deep Breathing. For some people this is a natural process, but if you have learned to breathe incorrectly, you will need to teach yourself how to do Long Deep Breathing until that becomes your new "natural" meditative breath.

Long Deep Breathing

Once you learn to breathe properly, you can learn Long Deep Breathing, a basic pranayam repeatedly mentioned in this book. The benefits are off the charts: it relaxes you, increases the flow of prana, prevents build-up of toxins in the lungs, stimulates endorphins, pumps the spinal fluid to the brain which in turn increases your energy, enhances intuition, adjusts the electromagnetic field, cleanses the blood, regulates pH, releases blocks from your energy meridians, aids physical and emotional healing, breaks subconscious patterns, channels pain conditioning, and manages negativity. Not bad for something free and easy.

How to Do Long Deep Breathing: Long Deep Breathing uses the full capacity of the lungs by engaging all three parts of the respiratory system: lower, middle, and upper. Go from low to high: to begin start by filling the abdomen, expanding the chest, and then lifting the upper ribs. Exhale in the reverse, expelling air from the top down. Master Long Deep Breathing and master yourself.

Breath of Fire

Another breath commonly discussed in kriyas and meditations throughout the book is Breath of Fire. This is one of the most common pranayams in Kundalini Yoga, and any discussion of Kundalini would be incomplete without it.

Breath of Fire strengthens the lungs, purifies the blood, balances the nervous system, boosts the immune system, and enhances oxygenation of the body. It is highly beneficial for addictions, including overeating and junk foods.

How to Do Breath of Fire: Breath of Fire is quick, rhythmic, and sustained. The inhale and exhale are equal, with no pause in between, at a pace of approximately 2-3 cycles per second. It is done through the nostrils with the mouth closed (unless stated otherwise specifically in a kriya). Breath of Fire is powered from the strength of the Navel Point, though not through any exaggerated pumping of the navel or huffing of the chest. To exhale, the air is expelled powerfully through the nose, by contracting the Navel Point back toward the spine rapidly. To inhale, the upper abdominal muscles relax and the breath comes in as part of a natural relaxation. The body stays relaxed throughout. Make sure that when you pull in your navel, you are exhaling. Don't allow your breath to reverse. *Do not practice Breath of Fire if you are heavily menstruating or more than 120 days pregnant. Breath of Fire is not recommended for children under the age of 8.*

Bandha

In Kundalini Yoga, we apply bandha, also called body locks, during asanas to move the flow of Kundalini energy up our spine in a controlled and precise fashion. They also serve to promote proper alignment and balance the flow of prana and apana (in and out flow of energy in the body). Basic body locks include Neck Lock, Diaphragm Lock, Root Lock, and the Great Lock.

Neck Lock or Jalandhar Bandh

As a general rule, Jalandhar Bandh is applied while chanting or doing pranayam. It assists good posture of the spine while sitting in meditation. It can regulate blood pressure to avoid the sudden shifts that can occur while doing kriya and help prevent dizziness. It allows the energy to flow up to the crown of the head unobstructed.

To apply Neck Lock: Sit comfortably with a straight spine, and lift your chest and sternum. Stretch the back of the neck up, tucking in your chin slightly. You should feel no strain in your neck. Make sure to relax your shoulders and upper back. The Neck Lock should not be forced, make it hard to breath, or otherwise be uncomfortable.

Root Lock or Mulbandh

The Root Lock balances the energies of the rectum, sex organs, and navel. It helps correct imbalances in sexual energy, whether too much or too little, and transforms it to creative energy. Often applied at the end of a meditation to seal the practice, its key purpose is to balance the energy at the Navel Center.

To apply Root Lock: Contract the muscles of the anus, then tighten the muscles of the sex organ, lifting the pelvic floor. Then contract the muscles of the lower abdomen up and in toward the spine. Do these three actions in a smooth, rapid succession. Breath may be held in or out during Mulbandh; follow specific instructions as noted in the particular kriya or meditation you are doing. *Do not apply Mulbandh if you are heavily menstruating or more than 120 days pregnant.*

Diaphragm Lock or Uddiyana Bandh

The Diaphragm Lock raises the energy up the abdomen, massaging the intestines and the heart. It is an important emotional integration tool. When applied it stretches the muscles between the ribs so that the entire rib cage can expand. As you pull the lock, the solar plexus is engaged, and it strengthens the fire element with you and opens the Heart Chakra, releasing kindness and compassion.

To apply Diaphragm Lock: This lock is only applied with the breath fully exhaled and held out. Inhale deeply, then exhale fully and pull the diaphragm up and back toward the spine. Although you don't directly engage the Navel Center, it will shift as the muscles of the diaphragm move. Keep the chest lifted and hold for 10-60 seconds based on your ability. Do not strain. *Do not apply Uddiyana Bandh if you are full from eating, heavily menstruating, or more than 120 days pregnant.*

The Great Lock or Mahabandh

This is a combination of all three locks above at the same time, while holding the breath out. It is generally practiced after pranayam or during kriya. It is said to rejuvenate and heal the body and can aid blood pressure problems, menstrual cramps, poor circulation, and other ailments. The glands, nerves, and chakras are all restored.

To apply the Great Lock: Exhale completely and apply Mulbandh; apply Uddiyana Bandh; apply Jalandhar Bandh.

YOUR THREE MINDS

The mind is matter in a subtle form. We tend to think of our physical bodies as being material and our minds as existing only in immaterial thought, but in yoga philosophy, the mind is material but more subtle than the brain, its physical carrier. Think of water in its three forms: ice, liquid, and gas. All three states are still water, just existing in different material states. Yogis believe that your body, mind, and spirit are all states of the one YOU, expressed in different states on the material plane. You can affect your mind and thoughts with things like food, meditation, and the energy of what you focus on. If you put good things into your mind, good things will come out of it. To master the mind, it's helpful to understand more about it.

Yogi Bhajan taught that there are three minds: Negative, Positive, and Neutral[19]. Many of the kriyas and meditations in this book have been chosen to balance one of the three minds, and as we balance mind, body, and spirit throughout the book, careful attention has been given to balancing all three of the minds throughout the process.

The Negative Mind sees the pitfalls, the Positive Mind sees the potentials, and the Neutral Mind assesses the input from both and responds from a neutral place. The Neutral Mind is also called the meditative mind. Each of these minds develops in different ratios in different people. It is very rare to see all three minds totally balanced, so you will likely recognize more of one rather than another in yourself. In general, people with low self-esteem and body image problems will have a weak Positive Mind or an overly developed Negative Mind.

The Negative Mind is very powerful and often misunderstood. It is the part of the brain that responds defensively to everything it encounters. Its ultimate role is to preserve and protect us. It calculates risk and finds potential pitfalls to keep us from harm. It's absolutely impossible for it to respond positively to anything; that is the role of the Positive Mind. When the Negative Mind is too strong, we become full of anxiety, fear, and self-doubt, but a Negative Mind that is too weak can leave you exposed to danger and foolish decisions. With a balanced Negative Mind, you have the ability to make calm and clear decisions.

The Positive Mind sees the possibility in everything. Its job is to calculate what is going right. It keeps the light shining strong no matter how dark things get. When your Positive Mind is strong, you have a good sense of humor and a strong sense of hope. You are full of bliss, joy, and ready to succeed. The Positive Mind corresponds to the Navel Center, to the seat of will, so a strong Positive Mind leads you to be action-oriented and organized. When the Positive Mind is weak, it will find your hidden traumas in your subconscious, blow them out of proportion, and reinforce negativity. In extreme cases, you can become paralyzed with negativity and feel like giving up entirely. When your Positive Mind is too strong, you can become rigid and dogmatic. Many people with eating disorders have an imbalanced Positive Mind.

The Neutral Mind is like a scale. It balances and weighs the information being offered to it by the Positive Mind (what could go right?) and the Negative Mind (what could go wrong?). It rises above agenda and the details of the world to give a more neutral and yet intuitive and compassionate determination of your best path. A strong Neutral Mind can evaluate and determine the best course within 9 seconds. A weak Neutral Mind means that you are at the mercy of the dueling Positive and Negative Minds; you will be changeable, have trouble making up your mind, get involved in a mental war with yourself, and be at the mercy of a roller coaster of emotions. The Neutral Mind slows that process down and allows you to develop your thoughts from an objective and compassionate place.

Beginning to balance your Positive and Negative Minds while making decisions from the Neutral Mind is a powerful turning point; understanding that your mind serves you, and that you are no longer at its mercy or subject to its whims, is deeply and profoundly empowering.

FALL IN LOVE WITH SEVA

Seva means selfless service and it is one of the most empowering tools we have to develop a strong sense of self-love and lift us out of our problems. Service to others is love in action. It allows you to step outside of yourself and your problems for a minute and gain perspective. One of the most healing parts of my journey has been spending time at a children's home in India, where I've taught meditation to the kids and helped raise funds to support them. Serving them not only releases my own heavy emotions, but it reminds me that there is so much outside of myself that matters in this world. It gives me perspective on my feelings about my weight and my body, and I'm able to see my concerns for what they are: nothing worth anywhere near as much time as I have given them already in my life.

I recall seeing a young boy one day with burns on his body. I asked someone how he got them and was told that he had been set on fire by soldiers in his village. As he played on the swing set in front of me—this young boy who had been through the worst the world had to offer, smiling as wide as the world, filled with joy and love for life—my first thought was, "I've never had any problems." I knew I had to start living with passion and happiness. All that held me back from starting to live my dreams—my perception of my weight, my long-held self-consciousness, my need for external validation—everything was in my mind, and my mind was something that I could learn to control. My mind literally side-stepped my own mental dramas about my weight and my image and shifted into a new paradigm of empowerment and grace. That little boy helped me awaken to this blissful fact: if you want a fast way to help yourself, go help someone else.

DO NO HARM

Whether you have an eating disorder, or you are simply self-conscious about the way you look, the most important aspect of yoga to assist you in your healing may be ahimsa, which is the practice of non-violence, or more literally, non-harm. To truly become a yogi, one who unifies oneself with spirit, nothing will be more important than the practice of ahimsa, where you work to not harm others, yourself, or your body. In order to live this life in deed, word, or thought, practicing self-love and compassion toward your own body, for being what it is, or not being what you wish it were, is a spiritual path that can bring enlightenment and liberation. Loving yourself isn't arrogance or conceit. Truly loving yourself has nothing to do with another, and self-love doesn't come at the expense of another. It is true union with the Divine within. What if you fell so in love with yourself that every morning you woke up praising the Divine creation within you, and every night you feel asleep with deep gratitude for your Body Temple? What if every inhalation was the Breath of Life and every exhalation the praise of the Universe? Practice non-harm. Live with ahimsa. Start again in your practice with every kind thought, every gentle word, and every loving deed.

I believe in myself.

CHAPTER 5

Beginning Your Journey

"Yoga is not about self-improvement, it's about self-acceptance."

~ Gurmukh Kaur Khalsa

CREATING A SACRED SPACE AND A BODY TEMPLE ALTAR

You don't have to have a special place to do Kundalini Yoga and Meditation. You can do it anywhere. I've done it in my living room, a studio, my bed, rock outcroppings next to rivers, even on airplanes. There is, however, a power in creating a sacred space for yourself and your practice. The more sacredness you bring into your space, the more room you make for sacredness in your life. In my own home, I have altars set up in almost every room, and I put things on them that inspire, uplift, and remind me of the Divine. When we look at the things that inspire us, it is easier to feel the sacredness in daily life, and we are reminded to take a moment to honor and acknowledge all that we are doing. Anything that helps you remember to say something kind to yourself is a very good thing!

I suggest you begin your journey by creating a sacred self-love altar. You can do this in any way you would like, but here is my suggestion for a wonderful altar to your Body Temple. Find a space to dedicate to an altar, even if it is just a dresser, or a shelf on a bookcase. Clean the space thoroughly. In the center of this altar place a photo of yourself. You may not yet see yourself as sacred, but on this journey you are the most sacred thing of all. Ideally, this photo would have your entire body visible, with no sections cut off. Take pink salt or sea salt, and sprinkle a thin line of salt all around your photo, symbolizing a protective energy around you that will assist you in healing and transforming negative energy. Around your own photograph, place images of great masters that inspire you. You could include images of Yogi Bhajan, the Goddess Lakshmi, Jesus, Amma, anyone who inspires you and holds a place of wisdom in your consciousness. If you cannot find a picture, you can write the name of the spirit, energy, or person who inspires you on a piece of paper. When you place their photo or their name on your altar, invoke their presence and ask them to be with you during your healing journey, to help you reconnect to your body and spirit in loving ways. Then begin to add things to the altar that connect you to nature. You may choose to add flowers, or some special crystals or stones. If you are inspired by crystals, for example, explore their use and meaning (I like to pair rose quartz, a powerful self-love tool, with malachite to heal the wounds of the heart). You may choose to add inspirational messages to your altar, such as "Bountiful am I, Beautiful am I, Blissful am I" or "I love myself" or simply words like "Healing" and "Miracle."

Once you have your altar set up in a way that you like, recognize that you have already taken a step to reconnecting with your sacred nature. When a person is fully aligned with their spirit, they cannot cause their own body harm in thought or deed. You may choose to further activate your altar with prayer, sacred music, or simply by speaking your own invocation. Come back to this altar every day to meditate, pray, do your practice, or simply be visually reminded that you are a beautiful spirit.

Creating a sacred altar is a powerful way to create harmony in your external environment and establish a physical reminder that you are making time for the sacred in your life. It is important to begin to see yourself as Divine and creating an altar that honors you is a wonderful first step.

I've taken this to heart in a number of ways, allowing my altar to spill out all over the house. There's a sign above my bedroom window that says, "You are Loved ... Always," and a hand-made computer cover that bears the words "I love you, Ramdesh! You're beautiful!" so that every time I go to do my work, check social media, or even write this book, I'm reminded to tell myself I love myself. These hidden and not-so-hidden reminders help me to never forget self-love and keep me from lapsing into bad habits and old patterns.

It may be difficult to feel like your heart is really in this process if you've spent years being unkind to yourself. Trust me anyway and give this a try. You will be surprised how helpful it is to aid you in replacing negative self-talk with positive self-talk, even if you have to trick yourself into it a little in the beginning. It was the same for me, but now it comes easily and feels absolutely Divine!

Put Away the Scale

For some, this will be the hardest part of this journey, but you cannot learn to identify as a spirit if you are constantly quantifying your body. Attaching yourself to the scale means that you believe your value is the number you see there. It triggers unhealthy patterns. During your healing journey, as you discover the power of being body positive, I encourage you to tuck the scale away. Hide it in the very back of your closet, or toss it out altogether. You can't weigh your spirit, and it is your spirit we want to care for most during this process.

What to Wear for Your Kundalini Yoga Practice

You don't have to wear something specific for doing Kundalini Yoga, and if you are the kind of person who spends hours every day obsessing over every little detail of how you dress and how you look, terrified about how people will see you, I ask you to treat yourself with enough kindness not to allow that to filter into your personal yoga practice. Yoga is what you do for yourself and for yourself alone. Even if you attend a Kundalini Yoga class with other people, much of the class is done with your eyes closed, and because this form of yoga is not based on the perfection of physical posture, you're not going to spend your time staring at your reflection in a mirror, comparing yourself to others or the teacher, and wondering why you're not perfect. In fact, if you are practicing with a mirror, I'd like to ask you to sit with the mirror at your back so you can't open your eyes every few seconds and check to see how you look. While honoring your Body Temple through the practice of Kundalini Yoga, relate to what is on the inside more than what is on the outside for a while.

It is recommended that you wear light, white clothing while doing Kundalini Yoga to boost your aura and your radiance. I recommend that you try the practice of wearing white, something that is a natural fiber, breathable, and allows for easy movement. Boosting your aura is going to help you feel better quickly and it can also serve you in going deeper into your meditation. You will also see many Kundalini Yogis wearing head wraps or turbans. This concentrates the energy of your solar center around your Crown Chakra and can increase your ability to meditate deeply and without distraction. It adjusts your cranial bones and can often make you feel like you can think more clearly. I encourage you to try it, especially while doing longer meditations involving chanting, such as Kirtan Kriya, where the use of a head wrap can help prevent headaches, or in the recitation of mantras, where it is traditionally done as a mark of respect to the sacredness of the words. Although it is not a mandatory element of the practice, it can considerably enhance your experience. You could also try a shawl or scarf draped over your head if you are uncomfortable with a head covering. This is a practice of love and joy; do what makes you happy and makes you feel good!

If you are used to wearing black or darker colors to make yourself look thinner, try wearing white during your practice for a change and see how much more radiant you feel when you dress to boost your aura! Dress regally and with self-care. Let yourself be comfortable!

Tune In Before Your Practice

Before beginning any of the Kundalini Yoga kriyas or meditations shared in this book, set a sacred space for your practice by tuning in with the mantra *Ong Namo Guru Dev Namo*.

To tune in, place your hands palm-to-palm at the center of your chest, shut your eyes and focus them in and up to the Third Eye Point between your eyebrows. Take a few long and deep breaths to center yourself into your body and connect with your physical form. Inhale deeply and as you exhale, chant *Ong Namo Guru Dev Namo* on a single breath. Inhale and repeat two more times. Always tune in with this mantra three times before beginning your practice of Kundalini Yoga.

Ong Namo Guru Dev Namo means that you are calling upon the infinite creative wisdom both outside of and within you to be present during your practice.

After chanting this mantra, dedicate your practice to your healing efforts for an added boost.

Closing Prayer After Your Practice

A beautiful tradition in Kundalini Yoga as taught by Yogi Bhajan® is to sing a simple blessing known as the Long Time Sun song, written by Mike Heron. It is a simple practice to bless yourself and others with the beautiful energy you create during your practice. It allows you to realize that your entire life is your practice, and can help you keep your sense of the sacred throughout your day. You can sing these words to yourself after your practice, listen to a recording of this song, or just chant one long *Sat Nam* at the end of each session to seal your practice.

LONG TIME SUN

May the long time sun shine upon you
All love surround you
And the pure light within you
Guide your way on.
Sat Nam!

HOW TO USE THIS BOOK

There are many ways that you can use this book. You can flip around and see what stands out to you intuitively. You can read it cover to cover and do one thing at a time. You can follow the program for Radical Self-Love outlined here. You can chant a mantra that feels right to you once, or for hours every day. You can mix and match. You can try the kriyas and meditations one at a time or choose one to practice for 40 straight days. Know this: you cannot do it wrong. There are no perfect kriyas or meditations just for you, nor any that would be wrong choices. They will all support you. If something resonates with you then you should definitely try it and continue it for at least 40 days. A long-term Kundalini Yoga practice can call for a meditation, mantra, or kriya to be repeated for 40, 90, 120, or even 1,000 consecutive days for mastery. If you miss a day, you begin again at day 1.

According to the teachings of Yogi Bhajan, here's what an extended practice of a kriya, mantra, or meditation can do for you when practiced consecutively:

40 Days: This breaks negative habits that limit your vibrancy.

90 Days: This establishes a new habit into your conscious and subconscious minds.

120 Days: This confirms the new habit that has been created by the energy of the kriya, meditation, or mantra. The positive effects of your practice become permanently engrained into your psyche.

1,000 Days: This allows you to master the effects of this practice as a soul for all your lifetimes.

Here's the secret: don't beat yourself up when you backslide or miss a day. Maybe you are struggling with compulsive overeating and you begin yoga and meditation, and for a few days you do great, until one night you fall off the wagon. Don't beat yourself up. You aren't a failure when you fall back into a habit. Kundalini Yoga gives you the strength and fortitude to keep up, to get back on the saddle and try again. Fall down seven times, stand up eight, goes the saying. Your journey doesn't have to be perfect to move forward. Just keep going forward.

Keep meditating, keep doing yoga, keep chanting. This won't fix your problems overnight, but it can immediately give you the support you need to find healing. If you are about to make unhealthy food choices, stop and use a pranayam that you find in the book, or step out of the kitchen and chant a mantra for a few minutes. Use these practices to form the backbone of your life, but also use them in a quick pinch to help you overcome your inner demons. You are not a failure and you cannot fail. To become more loving to yourself, you must also become compassionate. If you successfully get onto a healthy program, love yourself. If you slip up into restriction or purging or negative self-talk, love yourself. Every breath is a new moment and new opportunity to practice self-love. This is radical healing: you have the chance to create your life anew with every breath, and you cannot get it wrong. Love yourself, just as you are, and allow that love to transform you into who you want to be. In all things, practice love.

"Keep up and you will be kept up."

~ Yogi Bhajan

ASSESSING WHERE YOU ARE AND WHAT YOU NEED

It's not uncommon to feel overwhelmed by Kundalini Yoga, especially if you are new to the tradition. There are a ton of strange words, complicated mantras, and yoga sets and meditations that can all feel very new and overwhelming. For those of us who spend a lot of time feeling disconnected to our bodies, we can feel like we don't know what our bodies need or where to begin. Rather than becoming frustrated or overwhelmed and quitting before you start, try this simple three-part practice for self-assessment. This can help you ease into a physical or meditation practice. You can start with very short times, and there's no perfect result. You just notice what you think about (if your mind is wandering or bored, that's okay too). Don't judge your experience, just notice how you feel. Try taking notes on your experience. You will find that as you continue your practice, your self-assessments will change and how you feel inside will shift and evolve. Not every experience of meditation brings instant bliss and harmony; it's very common, especially when beginning a practice, to get irritated, bored, or anxious. Rather than running away from the uncomfortable emotions, give yourself the opportunity to sit with them and feel them shift or weaken in strength. This can be a major key to changing unhealthy patterns. Simple, but true; just like building muscles at the gym, some days are better than others, and it takes time to develop your Body Temple. Let's start your journey with an inner assessment of where you are now.

Meditation for Inner Assessment

Ramdesh's Insight:
Do you feel centered? Do you feel imbalanced? Where do you feel out of balance? Are you balanced in your body? Are you balanced in your mind?

Part One: To Know Your Inner Balance

Sit in Easy Pose with closed eyes and focus at the Third Eye Point (the point between your eyebrows). Bring your hands into Prayer Pose at the center of the chest, but then raise your left hand so it is higher than the right, and the right palm is resting on your left forearm, just below the wrist. Breathe deeply, taking very slow breaths. **Continue 3-11 minutes**.

Ramdesh's Insight:
What are you attracting to you? What is your vibrational point of attraction? Are you sending positive vibes or negative energy?

Part Two: To Know Your Inner Projection

Sit in Easy Pose with closed eyes and focus at the Third Eye Point (the point between your eyebrows). Take your thumbs and hook them into the hollows on either side of your nose, then press the base of your palms together and slowly touch the rest of your hands together, touching your fingertips together last. Breathe deeply, taking very slow breaths. **Continue 3-11 minutes**.

Ramdesh's Insight:
Are you strong and vital right now? Is your energy waning? Do you have the strength to continue on when things are difficult?

Part Three: To Know Your Inner Strength

Sit in Easy Pose with closed eyes and focus at the Third Eye Point (the point between your eyebrows). Place your hands right over left onto your Heart Center and press as hard as you can throughout the entire meditation. Breathe deeply, taking very slow breaths. **Continue 3-11 minutes**.

After Your Meditation:

After you finish this meditation, jot down your self-reflections below. What have you learned about how your body and mind truly feel right now? Are you ready to begin to heal? Can you tell where you most urgently need support in your physical body, emotional body, or mental bodies? Self-assessment exercises like this can be very helpful in understanding where you are today, and measuring changes as you continue with this program of Radical Self-Love.

NOTES ON MY FIRST SELF-ASSESSMENT:

I am enough.

CHAPTER 6

The Chakras

"Body is the temple of God."

~ Yogi Bhajan, October 12, 1988

One of the most beautiful and subtle aspects of your Body Temple is the chakra system. The human body is comprised of many energetic vortexes, but there are seven major chakras in the human body. In the tradition of Kundalini Yoga, the Eighth Chakra is said to be the Aura, the magnetic field surrounding the human body. The lower the chakra, the denser the energy associated with it. As you move up to the highest chakra, the energy becomes more refined. Prana powers the chakras and, when they are balanced and healthy, like doors they open to allow a greater force to flow through them. When a chakra is closed off, it limits the energy flow allowed through it and creates an emotional and sometimes physical imbalance. Kundalini Yoga helps to clear, open, and balance all the chakras.

Learning to open and balance your chakras can be an incredible tool when you're on a journey into self-love. By following your emotions and thoughts as a guidance system, you can discover which of your chakras may be out of balance. By opening each of your chakras and allowing the energy to flow, you can often move through major blocks quickly. Kriya, asana, mantra, and meditation can all open the chakras. You can also bring more of the associated color into your life as a form of color therapy.

FIRST CHAKRA OR ROOT CHAKRA

Color: Red
Themes: Security and survival
In Balance: Grounded, steady, centered, stable
Out of Balance: Fearful, lacking self-acceptance, concern for survival, weakness in physical body

The Root Chakra is where our foundation lies. If the Root Chakra is out of balance, we will feel deeply insecure and out of place. We will be ruled by fear and habit, and find it difficult to find our center. For many people with food and body issues, some traumatic experience triggered an imbalance in this chakra which began to manifest in our relationship to food and our own bodies. If there was a time when your body felt like an unsafe place to be, you could have developed a deep imbalance in the Root Chakra which manifested in a variety of ways. If you have feelings of constant fear, self-disgust, and feeling out of control, it's likely that your Root Chakra is out of balance. For many people with eating disorders and poor body image, this is a key chakra that needs strengthening. When the Root Chakra comes back into balance, we feel stronger and more stable. Fear turns to faith and we begin to trust ourselves, our lives, and our bodies again.

First Chakra Asana: Chair Pose

Begin in a standing position with feet shoulder-width apart and squat down until your thighs are parallel with the ground. Wrap your hands around the inside of the legs and place your hands on the top of your feet. Keep your back straight and breathe deeply; start with 30 seconds and build your way up to 3 minutes. Your chin should be slightly tucked in toward the ground unless you are very flexible, in which case you may do a more advanced version of the asana by raising your head and looking at the wall in front of you.

Chair Pose helps root you energetically to the earth and stabilize your relationship to the physical plane. In this position remind yourself that you are stable and grounded. Imagine yourself strong as steel.

 SECOND CHAKRA OR SACRAL CHAKRA

Color: Orange
Themes: Creativity, sexuality, relationships, emotions
In Balance: Creative, patient, good relationships, healthy sexuality
Out of Balance: Imbalanced sexuality, feelings of shame, unhealthy relationships, overly emotional

The Second Chakra holds our sexuality and emotions. A deeply creative force comes from this chakra and, if it is out of balance, we end up creating what we don't really want. When we don't honor our own creative power, and instead are ashamed of who we are, we often attract painful relationships. For many of us with food and body issues, because of that shame and lack of self-worth, we constantly search outside ourselves for validation. Compound that with the fact that many of us have also been a victim of sexual abuse. The feelings of shame, self-punishment, or worthlessness that stem from this type of trauma are all signs of an imbalanced Second Chakra. When we bring our Second Chakra back into alignment, we can feel our own creative power and innate worth.

Second Chakra Asana: **Frog Pose**

With your heels touching, squat down with your fingers touching the floor between your knees and your gaze straight ahead. Inhale as your raise your hips up and straighten your knees, keeping your fingers on the floor and your heels lifted off the floor and touching; allow your head to relax down. Exhale and bring your hips down, returning to your original position. Begin with 11 repetitions and work up to 108.

Frog Pose is a powerful anti-depressant that helps move energy through the Second Chakra and brings energy from the lower centers up to the higher centers of the body, assisting the rise of the Kundalini. While doing this posture, visualize yourself as a creative, dynamic being with much to offer the world.

THIRD CHAKRA OR SOLAR PLEXUS

Color: Yellow
Themes: Will power, commitment, self-esteem
In Balance: Inner balance, good health, self-confidence, being true to yourself
Out of Balance: Despair, greed, weakness, control issues

The Third Chakra is our will center. It holds for us a place of strength and balance. All the digestive organs are related to the Third Chakra, directing both physical and emotional digestion. For anyone with food issues, this is a key chakra. When it is weak, we have difficulty staying true to ourselves and conform to other people's views about who we should be. We can give in to greed and become overly judgmental. For people who tend toward overeating, placing too much food into the digestive system can be a way of trying to drown out emotions that become stuck in a weak Third Chakra and don't get processed in healthy ways; the excess food only serves to further clog this chakra. For others with food restriction tendencies, the denial of food can relate to withholding emotions and not dealing with them, not digesting them; but lack of food can leave this chakra without enough prana. All imbalances related to control, whether out of control or overly controlling, relate to imbalances in this will center. With a strong Third Chakra we become internally balanced and more self-confident.

Third Chakra Asana: Bow Pose

Lying on your stomach, grab your ankles and lift your upper body and legs off the ground. Let the head lift up naturally as your raise your chest, being careful not to strain your neck. Your knees will be a little bit apart. Begin with just a few seconds and lower your body back down. Build up to rocking back and forth on your stomach like a rocking horse for a few minutes or up to 108 rocks per day.

Bow Pose helps to engage and activate the Third Chakra. It massages the internal organs and assists in blood flow to the digestive system. While in Bow Pose, tell yourself that you are committed to healing, self-care, and recognizing your true value.

 FOURTH CHAKRA OR HEART CHAKRA

Color: Green
Themes: Love and compassion
In Balance: Loving, generous, forgiving, compassionate, kind
Out of Balance: Closed off, easily hurt, heartlessness, codependency

The Fourth Chakra is the love center of your body and relates to the thymus, lungs, and heart. When it is in alignment it is easy and natural to love ourselves and others; we forgive ourselves easily and treat our own bodies with compassionate care. When our Fourth Chakra is out of balance we can become cruel, unforgiving or overly emotional, and dependent on the approval of others. If your Heart Chakra is strong and balanced, you cannot hurt yourself or your body. If you work on relating to the world with love, then the influence of love in your life can heal and release much of the pain caused by self-harm and lack of self-esteem.

Fourth Chakra Asana: Baby Pose

Sit on your heels and bend forward until your forehead is on the ground. Extend your arms behind you, next to your body, palms facing up. Breathe deeply and relax into the pose. If you feel claustrophobic, spread your knees. Begin for 30 seconds until you can comfortably rest in this position for several minutes.

Baby Pose is a gentle restorative asana. The heart knows how to heal itself; you have only to give it the space and gentleness to do so. Spend time while in this position sending loving and compassionate thoughts to yourself. Be mindful of all of the things your body does for you, breathing, digesting, building cells and muscles, and recognize its good work. Using a restorative pose to allow your body to heal is an important part of self-love and provides the ultimate opportunity to begin to practice gentle, loving self-talk.

FIFTH CHAKRA OR THROAT CENTER

Color: Blue
Theme: Communication, self-expression, trust
In Balance: Expressive, honest, clear communication
Out of Balance: Inability to tell the truth or communicate clearly, insecurity, lethargy

If you have difficulty speaking your truth, listening to others deeply, or you suppress yourself from communicating authentically, your Throat Center is likely out of balance. Practices to restore the Throat Center's natural function can allow you to move through this behavior and come into alignment with both your own creativity and also expressing yourself in open, healthy ways. Yelling at ourselves or others, saying unkind or untrue words, and biting our tongue all contribute to an out-of-balance Throat Center. This can be especially challenging for people with eating disorders, because hiding the condition and lying about it are very common. Bulimics in particular, due to excessive vomiting and wear on their throat, benefit from Throat Center work. Opening and balancing the Throat Center will help bring authenticity and self-expression back to your life.

Ramdesh's Insight: Camel Pose can be very triggering for those who have experienced trauma. Practice self-love and allow intuition to guide your practice.

Fifth Chakra Asana: Camel Pose

Stand on your knees and press your pelvis forward. Lift your Heart Center and exhale as you slowly lean back until you can rest your hands on your heels or ankles. If you cannot lean this far back or you find that this pose is too emotionally triggering for you at this time, place your hands at the base of the spine and arch the Heart Center up and back. When you are in place, drop your head back completely.

Camel Pose helps you develop trust, in addition to working on nearly all the major organs and systems. Many people are challenged by leaning their head back unsupported. By breathing long and deeply in this asana, you come to realize that your breath supports you and all is well. In this position, remind yourself that you are safe, that you are worthy, and that you deserve to be heard.

SIXTH CHAKRA OR THIRD EYE

Color: Indigo
Theme: Intuition
In Balance: Clear vision, intuition, wisdom
Out of Balance: Confusion, depression, rejection of the spiritual

The Sixth Chakra helps you see your true purpose on earth. It allows you greater vision and clarity, and supports your projection for what you want to create. If your Sixth Chakra is blocked, you feel cut off from your spiritual source. You become confused and depressed, and life can feel meaningless. If you have ignored your intuition repeatedly or used drugs and alcohol, the flow of energy at this wisdom center can become blocked. An open Third Eye is helpful in healing your relationship with food and your Body Temple because you can see a life after and beyond obsession. You can see that you will feel better, feel renewed. Until your Third Eye comes back into balance, trust me and listen to my words: *You can heal your life, and you are already beautiful just as you are.*

Sixth Chakra Asana: Archer Pose

Archer Pose is a highly empowering pose that helps you develop a strong and positive connection to your physical body. It engages vision, determination, and grace.

Step your right foot forward 2 to 3 feet in front of your left. Turn your left foot in to 45 degrees and turn your right foot out; bend the right knee so that it comes over the right foot. Tuck in your tailbone and extend your left leg straight out behind you. Keep the torso over the hips. Now curl your fingers into your palms, leaving your thumbs straight up, and stretch your arms out as if pulling a bow and arrow. Your right hand will be extended in front and your left hand drawn into your chest. Open your eyes and look straight ahead at the tip of your right thumb. Keep your chin tucked slightly towards your chest and lift your heart. Keep this position for a few minutes and repeat on the other side. Feel strong and steady in this posture, visualizing yourself aiming a bow and arrow at your goals: total health and healing. Know that you are a warrior and you can succeed in all you desire.

SEVENTH CHAKRA OR CROWN CHAKRA

Color: Violet
Theme: Oneness
In Balance: Strong connection to your soul, unity with all
Out of Balance: Weak connection to spirit, fear of death

The Crown Chakra is located at the top of your head. It is the lotus flower of consciousness that unfolds with awareness and awakening. All energy from the infinite flow of the Universe comes through the Crown Chakra and flows into your physical body. If you are out of connection with your own soul, and you feel shattered and fractured, visualize light pouring into your Crown Chakra, filling you with radiance.

Seventh Chakra Asana: Ego Eradicator

Our ego can be an impediment to an open Seventh Chakra. A simple way of bringing healing to the ego is by using a powerful technique called Ego Eradicator. It increases your radiance and charisma, boosts your aura, and helps keep your energetic field strong.

Sit in Easy Pose and raise your arms up to a 60-degree angle, rolling your shoulders back and down so that your shoulders are away from your ears. Keep your elbows and spine straight. Apply a slight Neck Lock and lift your chest forward to open your Heart Center. Curl your fingertips on to the pads of your palms at the base of the fingers (not the base of your palms). Thumbs are stretched back, pointing straight up, above the head. Keep the lines from your heart to the tip of your thumbs straight. Close your eyes and concentrate above your head and begin Breath of Fire* for 1-3 minutes.

Ramdesh's Insight: You may extend Ego Eradicator up to 31 minutes for advanced practice.

To End: Inhale deeply, suspend your breath, and bring your thumb tips together, touching over your head. Open your fingers while your thumbs still touch, and then exhale as you sweep your arms, with palms open wide, down to the ground. Relax.

---

* For an explanation of Breath of Fire, see Chapter 4, age 50.

EIGHTH CHAKRA OR THE AURA

Color: White
Theme: Radiance
In Balance: Powerful projection, strong spirit, invincible quality
Out of Balance: Withdrawn, vulnerable to negativity and attack

Many yoga traditions do not include the Eighth Chakra, but in the lineage of Kundalini Yoga, the Aura is seen as the Eighth Chakra encompassing all the rest, like the sum of all chakras. Its location is the electromagnetic field which surrounds the body. If you want to attract positivity into your life, you must have radiance and a powerful Aura. If your Aura is dim or full of holes, you are vulnerable to negativity and attack. Without a strong auric field, it can become difficult to overcome challenges and feel good within yourself.

Eighth Chakra Asana: Triangle Pose

Triangle Pose boosts your Aura and delivers energy throughout your electromagnetic field. Place the palms of your hands with fingers spread wide and the soles of your feet onto the ground to form a triangle with your body. Lift your hips high in the air and settle your feet hip-width apart. Keep your torso in a straight line from fingertips to tailbone, and straighten your knees as best you can. Pull your chin in to create a straight line with your spine, taking care not to sway your back. Breathe deeply. Begin with 30 seconds and build up to 3 minutes.

BALANCING ALL THE CHAKRAS AS A WHOLE

Chakras are not isolated, but work together as a complete energetic system. You can focus on balancing one chakra at a time, or bringing them in harmony as a complete system through practicing meditations like the one below.

Seven-Wave Sat Nam Meditation

This meditation is a great introduction to Kundalini Yoga and will help you open your mind to new experiences. It's a lovely, calming way to begin a Kundalini Yoga practice, and brings all the chakras into alignment.

Sit in Easy Pose with a light Neck Lock. Close your eyes and turn them up to the Brow Point, the point between your eyebrows. Place your palms together at your chest in Prayer Pose. Your thumbs should touch your sternum.

Inhale deeply and with each exhale, chant the mantra **Sat Nam** in a seven-wave pattern, pulsing Sa-a-a-a-a-at in six waves (the *t* sound comes in only at the sixth wave) and Nam on the seventh wave. On each round of the mantra, thread the sound through your chakras beginning with the First Chakra. Each pulse of Sa-a-a-a-a-at goes through a different chakra, ending with Nam pulsing at the Crown Chakra, through the Aura out to Infinity. As the sound passes through a chakra, gently pull the area that is associated with that chakra. For the First Chakra, pull in the rectum; for the Second, pull in the sex organs; for the Third, pull in the navel; for the Fourth, pull in the heart; for the Fifth, pull in the throat; for the Sixth, the Brow Point; and for the Seventh, the Crown. Continue for 11-31 minutes.

To End: Inhale and exhale deeply. Relax.

I open my heart to self-love.

CHAPTER 7

Mantra: The Sound of Healing

"We are a simple, living, human being and we should watch our living, and hear our inner sound, which is pure love, pure life, pure existence."

~ *Yogi Bhajan, November 24, 1990*

WHAT IS MANTRA?

Mantra is a way of consciously creating the energy we want to experience. It brings light into the mind and allows the soul to shine, bringing you the joy that is your divine right. The science of mantra is based on projecting a specific energetic code through the mind that can have a predictable effect upon our energetic and physical bodies. Essentially, mantra is healing sound vibration; it's a way to sync up your mind with the vibration of the creative Infinity of the Universe.

Each mantra is like a cosmic mathematical formula that can alter the patterns and chemistry of the brain (with both physical and metaphysical effects) in a predictable way. It is important to keep the mantras as they are written; dropping or changing a word would be akin to dropping a number in a math equation—you couldn't expect to get the same result!

Mantra works on a number of levels. Both the meaning of the mantra and the rhythmic repetition of it, which stimulates the meridian points on the roof of the mouth, create the power of the mantra. The breathing pattern that results from a mantra is also highly beneficial, because control of the breath leads to control of your mood.

Chanting a mantra either silently or out loud is a method of directing the mind. All of our emotions, sorrow, joy, jealousy, elation, are vibratory frequencies that pattern our experience. The spiritual teacher Ernest Holmes once said, "Change your thinking, change your life." But for most of us, changing our habitual thoughts is highly difficult, and so by taking us out of the language of our minds (English, Spanish, or whatever language we think in) and using a language we aren't familiar with, we can code our energy bodies with a new pattern, one we don't resist. For example, if saying the affirmation "I love my body" feels impossible, you could use *Ang Sang** *Waheguru* (Ecstasy is dancing in every cell of my body) to connect to a vibrational code of self-love, affirming the beauty of our bodies, bypassing the ego and subverting the mind's resistance to a good-feeling thought, and thus overriding the habituated pattern of self-loathing. Our thoughts determine how we feel about everything. Mantra stops the mind in its tracks; you can't think, "You're disgusting! You're so fat!" while

* Note on pronunciation: Rhymes with "Ung Sung"

you are chanting *Aad Guray Nameh*. The mind will only be able to focus on one thing at a time; by using chanting to control our dominant thoughts, we can give our spirit the space to breathe in an otherwise constant state of self-belittling. We can rest, give ourselves a second to catch our right mind, and then make better choices.

We chant constantly, even if we aren't aware of it. Chanting can look like "I'm fat, I'm so fat, I'm too fat for anything or anyone." If every other word out of our mouth is "I'm too fat for _____" then that is the vibratory pattern we are establishing in our Body Temple and we're not going to feel like we're enough or worthy or beautiful. After so many repetitions, it becomes difficult for the mind to believe anything else, even when we are starving to death and all medical evidence points to that thought being completely and utterly wrong.

When we consciously chant a mantra, we are invoking its specific vibratory resonance and placing it into the field of our mind. So if the mantra is for prosperity, peace, happiness, intuition, or any multitude of other marvelous things, this is the vibratory pattern we are establishing in our field. It doesn't actually matter if we know the meaning of the mantra or not; it will still have an effect. The sounds themselves are encoded with meaning and vibratory range. It's not all about belief, nor is it placebo. It's a matter of the Universe itself using certain frequencies to manifest things. Mantras were developed by those who could hear and understand the language of the Universe. They then blossomed forth these combinations of sounds to harness specific vibratory patterns and allow us to mirror them back to the Universe in its own language of sound, light, and energy.

A deep understanding of mantra requires a deep understanding of our world. Everything is energy. Everything is vibrating. Even things like rocks, cars, and wood piles are vibrating, not just living things or musical harmonies. Everything is zinging away on one frequency or another. The highest vibration of all is that which some call God, and others call "The Universe," or "Divine Love Intelligence," or a "Higher Power." The name itself doesn't matter, only its high vibratory field. The higher we vibrate the closer we come to union with it. We literally raise our own vibrations to sync up with the highest vibration of all.

AFFIRMATION

Affirmation, which is the use of English words stating clearly a positive phrase or projection, is a form of mantra. It uses the same technique of filling the conscious mind with supporting thoughts. You can create your own affirmations. They should always be positive and non-judgmental. Creating a phrase like, "I am whole, safe, and enough," "I am healing every day in every way," or "I am loved, loving, and lovely" can help us to reconnect to self-love in a powerful and profound way. You can even try specific affirmations like, "I am recovering my health and happiness. I am beautiful, and I love myself." I love having affirmations around my house, either stuck onto mirrors or walls with Post-It notes or even engraved on stones. They serve as powerful reminders to hold love in my heart at all times and create a world of positivity around me.

One important extension of affirmation is to keep your words positive. Commit to only saying kind, positive, non-judgmental things about others, too. Do not engage in gossip or criticism about anyone else's body during your recovery (and if possible, your life). You can retrain your entire brain to default to kindness and self-care when you care to be kind to others, too.

THE SCIENCE BEHIND MANTRA

Yogic science explains mantra in a very precise way. The tongue as it moves in chanting hits the upper palate of the mouth. There are 84 meridian points located at the roof of the mouth. As you stimulate each meridian point, it sends signals to the hypothalamus. Think of your meridian points as the notes on a piano. When your fingers play the piano, particular strings are struck behind the scenes that create the resonance of a particular note. When you chant with your tongue, your hypothalamus responds to the placement of the tongue strike by sending particular signals. The correct series of notes on a piano creates a particular song; the correct sequence of words creates a particular mantra, which in turn creates a particular hormonal cascade in the brain and the body. Some combinations will be more harmonious than others; it is not random. Ancient yogis were very knowledgeable about the science of mantra, and these sounds were patterned with tremendous consciousness and awareness.

There are many different moods and sounds to the songs that can be created on a piano, just as there are many moods and results that can be created by different combinations of strikes on the meridian points of the upper palate. The hypothalamus programs the chemicals that go into your brain. It is connected to the pituitary gland by blood vessels and regulates moods, emotional behavior, sexuality, and even physical things like hunger and sleep. Each mantra programs the hypothalamus in a particular way. You can strengthen the immune system, balance different parts of the brain, regulate sleep hormones, and more. Emotionally, chanting can open up huge blocks. You can overcome depression, enhance your intuition, and simply awaken to feeling good now.

HOW CAN MANTRA HELP YOUR RECOVERY?

There are a number of ways that using mantra can support your recovery. At times when I felt myself overcome by the urge to purge, I used mantra as a way to push back the thoughts and regain control over my own mind. While I was attempting to heal my own bulimic patterns, instead of listening to "do it, do it, do it" in my mind until I caved, if I found myself triggered, I could use *Aad Guray Nameh*, a protection mantra, to literally protect myself from the thoughts until the urges passed. If you find yourself suffering from compulsive thinking that leads to compulsive, self-destructive, or unhealthy behaviors, look for one of the suggested mantras below as a starting point to finding the mantra that can work for you in this situation.

Mantra can also help your recovery by including it as a normal part of your self-care sadhana routine. Chanting mantras while you drive, or take a walk, or sit down to meditate, or any opportunity you have to fit them into your day, can create a powerful savings account of good energy. As you build up more and more good energy in your body and mind, it is easier to make good choices. If you fill yourself up with negativity, it's very hard to feel positive.

With a sustained practice, for example 40 days of chanting a mantra for 11 to 31 minutes, you can make significant changes to your life. If you have hours to spend obsessing over your weight, you have time to chant. Start by giving yourself 11 minutes a day to chant a mantra, and see if you don't notice feeling better. If you've never chanted or meditated before, I wouldn't be surprised if you felt a little silly. The typical Western cultural program is to consider this "weird." But I guarantee you that eating-disordered behavior feels awful, so even if you think you can't live without it right now, giving anything that could help a shot—no matter how weird—is worth trying. So if you are feeling like mantra might be a little too weird for you, do us both a favor and suspend your judgment until you try it and see if you are affected positively by it. If you are still resistant and feel you are too busy, try replacing your regular commute music with mantra. Some of my most transformational moments with mantra have come while driving and chanting along.

Mantra can also be used passively. You can listen to it while working or play it in your environment to create a sacred healing space. Making your space feel good and infused with the energy of healing and power can help you find the strength to heal. Play mantra while you sleep, work, cook, or do almost anything! The more focused your attention is on a mantra, the deeper it can work on you. Even if you don't chant or meditate to mantra, allowing it to fill the space around you can help shift things in your life.

HOW TO USE A MANTRA

Mala Japa

Mala Japa means repetition of a mantra on a mala. Some people use a mala as an optional tool for mantra recitation, similar to a rosary. Made most often with 108 beads (both the number of infinity and the number of the nadi points, or energy centers, within the body), you move your fingers around a mala reciting one round of the mantra for each bead. A mala is a spiritual tool that helps you keep track of your mantra practice and absorbs the good effects of the mantra so that you can wear it throughout your day, infusing your energy field with the power of the mantra. You may find that wearing the mala that you also use for mantra practice reminds you throughout the day of your commitment to healing and recovery.

Recitation

Some people use powerful and clear recitation of a mantra as their form of practice. Similar to how you would use an affirmation (imagine yourself saying "I am worthy!" loud and clear), recitation is a verbal projection of a mantra. Usually this is done between 11 to 108 times for any one mantra.

Chanting Aloud

The most common form of mantra practice within Kundalini Yoga, chanting a mantra is its own form of spiritual practice, and the one that I used most often for my own recovery from eating disorders. For me, the energy and power that I created within me while chanting was something that I could feel immediately, and the peace that it brought me created powerful, quick, and lasting transformation. I still chant every day, whether for hours or for just a few minutes. I love everything about it. It lights me up. Chanting accelerates the power of the mantra into the meridian points of the upper palate; it opens the Throat Center (the creative, self-expression, and truth centers), soothes the Heart Center bringing love and peace within, and brings your energy into complete alignment. You can chant while meditating, sitting in a prayerful pose, or while moving around. If you sit with a straight spine and close your eyes, you may find the power of the mantra is magnified and you can feel greater effects from your chanting, but experiment with what works best for you. If you can find what is called kirtan, or a group chanting experience, definitely try it. Chanting as a group is one of the most powerful practices I have ever experienced and has given me tremendous meditation highs.

Silent Chanting

Chanting silently does work, although it has a different effect than chanting out loud because you do not engage the meridians at the roof of your mouth. It can still have a powerful effect and is a form of chanting I often recommend to those who are afraid of being judged by others. Instead of avoiding mantra altogether in public situations, chanting silently gives you a way to connect to a mantra and use it to overshadow negative self-talk. When using silent mantra, apply liberally and repeat. You can never have too much mantra floating through your mind.

Deep Listening

Listening is another powerful way of experiencing mantra. Try attending a sacred chant concert or listening to a recording of a mantra by an artist who is fully immersed in the power of the mantra. Sit and listen with all your mindful attention to a recording of these mantras and see how it makes you feel. I began my own healing journey with mantra by listening intently to the recordings of Snatam Kaur and Nirinjan Kaur. It completely changed my life. The beauty and peace that I heard blessed me in countless ways. Now, I am blessed to have married a kirtan artist. My husband Harnam chants every morning and keeps the vibration of sacred mantra strong in our home. Allow the beauty of the mantras to fill you up and open your heart.

Meditations

Many meditations in Kundalini Yoga involve chanting a mantra, sometimes aloud and sometimes silently. Sometimes they involve deeply listening to mantra. If you are wanting to experience a particular mantra in deep meditation, look at some of the meditations in this book for one that inspires you.

The Effects of Chanting Times

You will often see a pattern in the lengths of time for chanting in meditations. You'll notice a lot of meditations use 11 minutes or 31 minutes, for example. But if you are just going to use chanting as its own meditation, how do you know its effect on your body? Here's a helpful chart to show you how you are impacting your Body Temple through the power of mantra and meditation according to the Teachings of Yogi Bhajan® [20].

3 minutes: affects your electromagnetic field, circulation, and blood
7 minutes: affects brain patterns and increases strength of your magnetic field
11 minutes: affects your nervous and glandular systems
22 minutes: affects your three minds (Positive, Negative, Neutral) and clears the subconscious mind

31 minutes: affects all the cells in your body and balances your endocrine system
62 minutes: affects your frontal lobe of the brain, pituitary and pineal glands. The mantra works through your physical, mental, and emotional bodies and you begin to be in communication with the Divine within you.
2 ½ hours: affects your psyche in its co-relation with your magnetic field so that your subconscious mind is strongly imprinted in the new pattern by the surrounding universal mind. You completely remake your psyche.

FINDING YOUR MANTRA*

You can't go wrong with any of the suggested mantras in this book. Try them all. You can choose a mantra intuitively. Think of your heart as a lock and the mantra as a key. Feel what is going on in your heart and see if one unlocks something deep inside of you and brings you a greater sense of peace. You can also choose a mantra consciously. If you know you need help changing negative thoughts to positive thoughts, for example, consider using the mantra *Ek Ong Kar Sat Gur Prasad, Sat Gur Prasad Ek Ong Kar*. By using a mantra that you know works for something specific, you can create that energetic effect for you. One of my favorite teachers has said to me that when you read something and it excites you, it's a sign that it is for you, so if you are reading any of the suggested mantras and one draws you to it, that's for you!

The mantras included in this book are all Kundalini Yoga mantras that have been given to us through the lineage of Yogi Bhajan, the Master of Kundalini Yoga. Most of the mantras given by Yogi Bhajan have their origin in the sacred spiritual texts of the Sikhs of India and are in a language known as Gurmukhi, but they work for everyone and anyone can use these mantras regardless of their religious or spiritual path.

There are many mantras in the tradition of Kundalini Yoga. The mantras that follow are a few suggestions that you may find useful on your healing journey, but they are by no means an exhaustive list. There are many mantras that may soothe and heal your spirit. If these inspire you, seek out more!

---

* **A Note on Translations:** Translations are a fluid art; there are many ways to translate mantra. Words rarely have exact translations and some translations are more poetic than linear. Many of the translations featured in this book were shared by Yogi Bhajan's wife Bibiji Inderjit Kaur Khalsa in *Mantra: Personal Guidance through the Power of Word*, published by the Kundalini Research Institute, with a few noted exceptions.

These suggested mantras are powerful, sacred healing tools. They are not to be taken lightly or flippantly. For many people, these mantras form the core of their spiritual paths and are said to be living manifestations of the Divine. Please use them respectfully. They have great power to assist you in your healing journey. You may choose to cover your head out of respect for these sacred words. Treat them as sacred, and allow even that small gesture to teach you how to treat yourself more sacredly, too.

BOUNTIFUL BEAUTIFUL BLISSFUL: Mantra for Self-Love

Bountiful Am I, Beautiful Am I, Blissful Am I

Chances are you have spent a significant portion of your life saying unkind words to yourself. Maybe you glance in the mirror and make a face; maybe you hide from the mirror altogether. Maybe you see photographs of yourself and say "ugh!" I've spent more than my share of time crying in front of the mirror, heartbroken by the difference between what I saw and what I wanted to see. Every time we put ourselves down, our aura shrinks a bit. Our ability to attract opportunities diminishes, and our radiance dims. The bottom line is that the voice inside your head that puts you down is a mean liar. You've got to hear this: the voice in your head that is unkind is not you. It is shadow, imbalance, ego, and duality. You are bountiful, beautiful, and blissful. Every human being is born into this life with this inheritance. No matter who has said what to you and no matter what you have said to yourself, unless it sounds like "I am bountiful, beautiful, and blissful" you aren't talking about the realest, most precious part of you.

It's time to honor the preciousness of you. It's time to claim your bountiful, beautiful, blissful birthright. However you say this, however you sing it or chant it or make it a part of your life will benefit you. This is something everyone with eating disorders should be saying to themselves over and over. Listen up: You are Bountiful, You are Beautiful, You are Blissful. You don't have to believe it at first, but you will find that with repetition it will sneak into your consciousness until you are able to replace negative programming with positive radiance. These words help you come to a place of deep self-love and positivity. If no one else has ever said these things to you, or in fact, may have said the exact opposite, then you need to say them to you now. And if you're like me, they will be some of the hardest words you ever have to say. But if you can come to a place where you feel bountiful, beautiful, and blissful, it will be very difficult for eating disorders or a lack of body acceptance to maintain a foothold in your life. When you realize just how worthy you are of love and health, peace and happiness, then it becomes difficult for the vibration of all that runs counter to these beautiful things to exist within you. Prosperity, beauty, and joy; reawaken into loving the true you.

GURU RAM DAS:
Mantra for Miracles

Guru Guru Waheguru Guru Ram Das Guru
Great is the wisdom that flows through the one who serves the Infinite

This mantra was given to Yogi Bhajan by the great master Guru Ram Das in his astral self[21]. Known for his great humility and ability to heal and create miracles, Guru Ram Das protects all those who call upon him. Many miracles have come from chanting this mantra. If you need healing, protection, and miracles, chant this mantra. When you don't know what else to do, chant this mantra. If you're at the end of your rope, chant this mantra. It is an extremely powerful energetic code and you can use it in any situation. It gives you immediate access to the Neutral Mind. Allow the possibility of miracles to come into your life; heal your body, mind, and spirit with this mantra.

AAD GURAY NAMEH:
Mantra for Protection

Aad Guray Nameh, Jugaad Guray Nameh,
Sat Guray Nameh, Siri Guru Devay Nameh
I bow to the primal Wisdom
I bow to the Truth that has existed throughout the Ages
I bow to the True Wisdom
I bow to the Great Divine Wisdom

This mantra creates a great protective shield around you. It taps you into the power of surrendering to something that is high vibration. When we are addicted to our disorders and compulsion, we surrender to their low vibration; when we surrender to positive, uplifting vibrations, rather than being weak, we are actually filled with immense strength. When we surrender and bow to the force that created the cosmos, we are filled with protective grace. Yogi Bhajan said this mantra "clears the clouds of doubt and opens us to guidance and protection[22]."

I have used this mantra to protect myself from the compulsive, addictive thoughts of bulimia. In a late stage of recovery, when I was doing well and feeling well, out of nowhere, I once felt very pushed and driven by my inner addiction to binge and purge. The urge to purge was intense and my mind dropped back into my compulsive patterns, strongly driving me to do it. I pushed back by silently chanting *Aad Guray Nameh*, imagining that the thoughts weren't me at all. I visualized the compulsion as a force that was attacking me from the outside, and I chanted *Aad Guray Nameh* to create a powerful ball of golden light that shielded me so that the thoughts couldn't get in. This was so successful that the thoughts simply went away. The mantra held me in a protective light. Let it work for you, too.

WAHEGURU:
Mantra for Joy

Waheguru

There is no direct English translation for this word.
Wahe is indescribable bliss and Guru brings us from darkness to light.
Waheguru is complete ecstasy in Divine Wisdom

This mantra expresses the incredible feeling of going from ignorance to wisdom; it expresses the joy that comes from waking up to the ecstasy that is the Infinite Divine. This is a destiny-triggering mantra, an awakening mantra. Chant this when you feel the need to connect to the Divine and dwell in Divinity. Simply chanting this simple mantra can bring you to a state of deep peace, awareness, and joy. It's like singing to yourself over and over, "The Ecstasy of the Infinite Divine is right here, right now." And doesn't that thought feel good, right here, right now, where you are? This is the mantra I find myself chanting every morning to get my head right to begin the day. When I start with this ecstasy, it makes it easier to stay in love with myself and all creation, all day.

WAHEGURU WAHEJIO:
Mantra for Purifying the Ego

Waheguru Waheguru Waheguru Wahejio
Great beyond description is the experience of God's Wisdom;
the experience of the Soul merged in the Divine

This simple mantra contains a powerful energy. Yogi Bhajan said that it "soothes the wounds of life with the infinite bliss this mantra induces[23]." It can purify the ego, release inner anger, and bring bliss into your life.

Waheguru is an expression of indescribable bliss. It's the feeling of "Wow! The energy that takes me from darkness into light is real and it's here!" Three times you remind yourself of the extraordinary ecstasy of awakening to the presence of the Infinite within you, and then you unify this joy with your own soul by chanting *Wahejio*. *Jio* is a term of affection. It means "soul," but it is like saying "precious soul" or "dear friend." The experience of your own soul can bring you immense joy.

An unhealthy relationship with our body begins when we identify as a body instead of a spirit. When we think the sum total of our worth as human beings is in being skinny, and that we're only good enough if the scale reaches a certain number, we've lost connection to our soul. Our soul has no weight; it is just pure love and light. When we wake up to the beauty of the Universe and the fact that our own soul is as beautiful as the cosmos, when this awakening reaches deep into our being, then we can be released from the clutches of our ego, which tells us we are less than, not good enough, or ugly. We are released into the arms of our soul and can experience ourselves as whole, perfect, and beautiful, just as we are.

If anger bubbles up and you can't think of any healthy way to release it but to cause self-harm, quickly pull this mantra into your consciousness and use it. The anger that you might turn inwards onto yourself or lash out with at another will dissolve or diminish.

PAVAN GURU: Mantra for Energy

Pavan Pavan Pavan Pavan Par Paraa Pavan Guru
Pavan Guru Waheguru Waheguru Pavan Guru
The Divine Breath From Beyond the Beyond
Breath is the Guru, the Experience of the Divine

This mantra calls the powerful healing energy of prana into your presence—in spades. When we constantly deplete our bodies through overeating, purging, under-eating, laxative use, over-exercising, or critical thinking, our pranic energy dips critically low and we feel listless, lethargic, and sick. Eating disorders deplete our life force incredibly quickly because they combine negative self-talk with physical punishment. If you don't have enough prana, you're not going to feel good. You're not going to have vibrant energy to do all the things you want to do and that your spirit came here to do. This is especially true for anorexics, who are generally exhausted, having depleted their bodies of essential nutrients and life-sustaining prana. This mantra helps to restore pranic energy to your body[24]. Heal your body with an infusion of energy like a vitamin shot for the spirit.

ANG SANG* WAHEGURU: Mantra for Awakening the Infinity Within

Ang Sang Waheguru
The Infinite Being is within me and vibrates in
ecstasy in every molecule and cell of my being

When chaos takes over your life, filling your days and nights with pressure, fear, tension, and stress, throw a wrench into the gears of your brain and stop it from spiraling further out of control by chanting this mantra.

This mantra creates a vibration that allows your psyche to readjust itself and eliminates haunting thoughts[25]. When you feel like you've split into a thousand pieces and there is only chaos surrounding you, this mantra will gradually pull each part of you back into your center. It connects the limited consciousness

---

* Note on pronunciation: Rhymes with "Ung Sung"

of your human self with the limitless great Self and so lifts you out of the chaos and delivers you to your truest vibratory frequency.

It also allows you to connect to your physical body in a positive and loving way, which is crucial for recovering from an eating disorder or any form of self-loathing and dishonoring of your Body Temple. After berating your body for not being good enough, this mantra refutes that in a powerful way, pushing back against the negativity with equal if not greater force. Not only is your body good enough, but every cell is filled with Infinite love and is vibrating with the power of the Universe. Not too shabby an affirmation, and easy enough to remember in a pinch if you catch your mind saying something negative.

SAT NAM: Mantra for Truth

Sat Nam

True Name; Truth is my identity

The most prevalent of all mantras in the Kundalini Yoga tradition is at once very simple and very complex. You'll hear this mantra used as a greeting, and as a part of many kriyas and meditations. It's the default mantra and it is suggested to chant it in your head constantly on each inhale and exhale. Try it now: inhale *Sat* and exhale *Nam*.

What is *Sat Nam*? In simple terms, *Sat* means Truth and *Nam* means name or vibration. As a greeting, saying *Sat Nam* is a bit like saying "I see your true nature" or "I recognize the divinity within you." It is a way of acknowledging that at our essence is *the* Essence. Truth, which is bigger than any human truth, isn't a matter of right or wrong or even a concept that we can clearly articulate. It is simply an acknowledgment that the Great Mystery is who we are.

The vibration of the mantra itself is important. *Sat* has a vibration that reaches upward through the Crown Chakra. It is an etheric vibration, as the meaning of "Truth" here isn't tangible but is more etheric. *Nam* is "name" but more importantly, it is a vibration. The word itself carries a vibration that makes the Divine manifest into the earth plane. *Nam* is a grounding vibration, a manifesting vibration; it acknowledges the Infinite made manifest as a vibration in this world. If you meditate very carefully upon the vibration of *Sat Nam*, you can feel the flow of energy moving from the Etheric (Sat) to the Material (Nam). Chanting *Sat Nam* reaches up into the etheric plane and pulls the vibration of Infinity into your awareness, your consciousness, and your physical world.

This mantra is more than what it means in translation. It is an experience. By chanting *Sat Nam* or meditating upon it with your breath, you call into your awareness the state of the vibration of truth. You create an internal experience of what these words represent. Truth, enlightenment, consciousness, and above all awareness, come into your experience.

This mantra can be very powerful for people with low self-esteem, poor body image, or full-blown eating disorders because it forces you to remember what is true: we are light, we are love, we are peace, and we are worthy of good. It awakens your soul. So when our mental self-talk is negative, harsh, and cruel, it's not in alignment with our Universal *Sat Nam*, and it is therefore an untruth. There are no exceptions to *Sat Nam*. Every single one of us has the vibration of Infinity within us. There is no "She's good, but I'm bad." Anything outside of the integrity of the truth of our goodness is a bold lie told by our egos to keep our spirits small. At some point everyone with an eating disorder or low self-esteem has bought into that lie. *Sat Nam* is a mantra that can recall your spirit back to the truth.

RA MA DA SA:
Mantra for Healing

Ra Ma Da Sa Sa Say So Hung

Sun, Moon, Earth, Impersonal Infinity, Thou,
Totality of Infinity, personal sense of merger and identity,
Infinite vibrating and Real, I am Thou.*

This mantra doesn't really have a tight translation. Its meaning is beyond the meaning of its linear combination of bij sounds. It's a sound frequency for deep healing, by tuning the soul to the vibration of the Universe, which is pure and

* Translation from *The Aquarian Teacher* by Yogi Bhajan.

without disease or pain. This mantra holds within it eight sounds that stimulate the Kundalini flow within the central channel of the spine for healing[26]. It brings balance into the core of our energetic body and floods it with new energy.

> *Ra* means the sun; connecting with that frequency gives you energy.
> *Ma* means the moon; it aligns you with receptivity.
> *Da* is the energy of the Earth, grounding you in your roots.
> *Sa* is Infinity and as you chant this, your energy rises upwards and outwards, drawing in the healing of the Universe.
> When you chant *Sa* a second time, you pull the energy of Infinity into you.
> *Say* is a way of honoring the all-encompassing Thou. It is personal, like a secret name for God.
> *So* is a vibration of merger.
> *Hung* is the Infinite, the vibrating reality. It is the essence of creation.
> (*So Hung* together means, I am Thou.)

Imagine a prism catching the light of the sun and refracting it out into a rainbow. This mantra does something similar with the healing energy of the Universe. It grabs onto the healing elixir of the Divine and allows you to steer it in a particular direction, either into yourself, another person, the whole planet, or anything on which you focus your intention.

In many traditions, healing is said to occur when you raise your vibration into Divine Alignment. According to the Law of Attraction, healing must occur if your vibration matches it. This mantra is a way of raising your vibration to the frequency of Divine Healing.

If you or someone you know suffers from an eating disorder or negative body image, they need healing. The fact is, we all do. Healing isn't the same thing as a cure. You won't necessarily chant this for a few days and never struggle again with disordered eating or negative self-image, but it is a gentle, loving tool for recovery and transformation.

GOBINDAY MUKUNDAY:
Mantra to Remove Subconscious Thoughts

Gobinday, Mukunday, Udaray, Aparay,
Hariang, Kariang, Nirnamay, Akamay
Sustainer, Liberator, Enlightener, Infinite,
Destroyer, Creator, Nameless, Desireless

Imagine there's a room in your mind that contains all of the thoughts you have ever thought, all the images you have ever seen, and every sound you have ever heard. All of these imprints are stored on shelves, cabinets, couches, and spill out onto the floor. As you go about your day, you don't look into this room. You do your work, chat with your friends, browse the internet all from the main living room of your house. This main room is your conscious mind. What you realize you are thinking about and doing is happening in the conscious mind. But that back room, with all that storage, is your subconscious mind; all the things you don't think about still exist (a movie you watched 20 years ago, the time when you were 8 that you cut your finger on a nail, principles of physics you never quite learned in school). All the negative things you've ever said about yourself hang out in this room. For all of us, this room is cluttered. It's full to bursting with lost memories, fears, and anxieties; wild tangents your mind took that never had any basis in reality. Sometimes the back room is so full of trash you can't shut the door and it spills out into the main room, your conscious mind. You suddenly act fearful for no reason, become worried by unfounded thoughts, think a nasty thought about yourself for no reason. Clearing the subconscious mind creates a feeling of order and calm in the conscious mind and releases generalized fear and anxiety that seem to have no known cause.

Gobinday Mukunday is a powerful tool to clear the subconscious mind and eliminate deep-seated blocks, notably blocks to your own self-esteem[27]. Yogi Bhajan also said this mantra could balance the hemispheres of the brain, which is crucial to people who suffer from compulsive eating, and brings patience and compassion to the listener. That means patience and compassion for yourself, too, not just for other people, which is critical in recovery. Relapsing isn't failure; it's simply a step along the way to ultimate health and healing. If you treat yourself compassionately and patiently, and release the subconscious patterns that affect your choices, recovery becomes much smoother and long-lasting and you will feel better faster. This mantra will also allow you to rebuild your own confidence and self-esteem.

If you find yourself plagued by nightmares or night terrors, as many with eating disorders do, I would suggest chanting this mantra for 11–31 minutes before bedtime to release images from your subconscious mind so they don't bubble over into your dreams. Gradually, less and less will spill over, and your mind will become a well-ordered sacred space once again.

ARDAS BHAEE:
Mantra for Powerful Prayer

Ardas Bhaee, Amar Das Guru, Amar Das Guru, Ardas Bhaee,
Ram Das Guru, Ram Das Guru, Ram Das Guru, Sachee Sahee
The prayer that has been made to Guru Amar Das is guaranteed by Guru Ram Das. The miracle is complete.

Letting go is part of life. We let go of each breath, each heartbeat, each year. Life moves forward, never backward. We become very accomplished at letting go, and yet, it is so easy to fight to hold onto things, including our eating disorders or low self-esteem. So many people who are anorexic or bulimic fight literally to the death to hold onto their disordered thinking and behaviors. Many people have tremendous trouble letting go of their habits and patterns and ways of thinking.

Here's where the struggle begins: We are eternal beings in bodies that die. We are limitless creatures stuck in an elaborate illusion of limit. We are spirits who are tricked by the ego into thinking we are bodies. When we identify with the illusion, letting go of what we hold onto so fiercely terrifies us. If we identify only as a body-who-must-get-thinner-no-matter-what, then the prospect of healing feels like dying. But if we identify with our Infinite nature, with our True Self, with the boundless creativity of the Universe, we begin to realize that letting go of that which no longer brings us joy is the perfection we've been seeking all along. We can't think our way into this peace or growth. We can't reason our way into this knowing. We must experience a connection with the larger plan to know this gentle grace. We must reach out to the Infinite and ask, "Are you sure?" in order for our own soul to sing out, "Yes!"

If we continue to identify as a body instead of a spirit, the statistics will carry us away and break us down. This is life or death for many. You are *not* your body. You *have* a body. You are a *spirit*. Letting go of our disordered and self-abusive patterns honors the spirit; it allows us to unfold into who we truly are.

Choose the pain you need to let go of. Choose the fear, the anger, the thing you did years ago that you can't forget. Choose the situation you are ready to leave behind and then chant this mantra.

Ardas Bhaee is a mantra for answered prayers. It's hope when you're at the end of the road. It's a prayer when you don't know what to say or what to pray for. This mantra calls upon Guru Amar Das and Guru Ram Das (who represent the Hope of the Hopeless and the Lord of Miracles), two great masters of the Sikh lineage. It begins by affirming that what you are saying is a prayer, but this mantra doesn't belong to a religion. It is a transformational tool that belongs to all. When you use this mantra, you connect with their powerful energies. When you chant *sachee sahee* at the end, you release it and let it go, knowing that your prayer is heard and it is done.

This is the mantra of answered prayers, of moving beyond difficult situations, and gracefully letting go[28].

EK ONG KAR SAT GUR PRASAD:
Mantra for Positivity

Ek Ong Kar Sat Gur Prasad, Sat Gur Prasad Ek Ong Kar

I know this by the Grace of the True Guru. I know this by the Grace of the True Guru. That God and We are One.*

It is easy to get caught up into a cycle of escalating negativity. It can be very difficult to stop the mind in its tracks, especially if we've allowed our negative thoughts free reign for a long time. The more meditation you do, the more in control of your mind you become, and the less your negative thoughts spin out of control. However, gaining control over negative thoughts is especially challenging for people with eating disorders and poor body image because negative thoughts feed into our insecurities and reinforce our self-punishing habits.

---

* Translation from *The Aquarian Teacher* by Yogi Bhajan.

Ek Ong Kar Sat Gur Prasad is a powerful mantra that can stop negativity in its tracks. It transforms negative energy into positive energy[29].

One of the most sacred of all mantras, it is often recommended to chant the mantra *Aad Guray Nameh, Jugaad Guray Nameh, Sat Guray Nameh, Siri Guru Devay Nameh* first, in order to create a sacred space and energy around you before you begin chanting *Ek Ong Kar Sat Gur Prasad*. This mantra is the only Kundalini mantra that comes with a warning. This is such a powerful and creative mantra that you must watch your thoughts and actions after you chant it. You will be in such a state of manifestation that your thoughts will accelerate into being. Luckily, the energy within the mantra itself will help you switch your thoughts to the positive. It takes your own negative thought, stops it in its tracks, and reverses it into positivity. A thought rides into your consciousness to be processed with *Ek Ong Kar Sat Gur Prasad* and comes out pure with *Sat Gur Prasad Ek Ong Kar*.

This mantra can show you that your body is a temple through which knowledge and bliss fill you to overflowing. This is directly opposed to the typical mental pattern of someone with unhealthy self-image. Instead of seeing your body as betraying you by not being enough, you instead see it as a temple and a channel through which goodness comes to you. Instead of being nothing, your physical form is everything.

Try it. Sing it when you are feeling down or your thoughts are spinning out of control. Chant it to get control over your own negativity. Feel the blessings of the Infinite within your Body Temple.

CHATTR CHAKKR VARTEE:
Mantra for Overcoming Fear

Chattr Chakkr Vartee Chattr Chakkr Bhugatay
Suyambhav Subhang Sarab Daa Sarab Jugatay
Dukaalang Pranaasee Diaalang Saroopay
Sadaa Ang Sangay Abhangang Bibhutay
Thou art pervading in all the four directions,
the Enjoyer in all the four directions. Thou art self-illumined,
profoundly beautiful, and united with all.
Destroyer of bad times, embodiment of mercy.
Thou art ever within us. Thou art the everlasting
*giver of undestroyable power.**

If you are feeling anxious, filled with fear, or overcome with phobias, perhaps about gaining weight or appearing sexually unattractive, this mantra can help. It is said to give the experience of victory to those who connect with it, and that could be useful to anyone needing victory in overcoming an eating disorder. According to Yogi Bhajan, "*Chattr Chakkr Vartee* is the mantra for the Heart Center; it gives direct energy to it. When you are sinking, if you know this mantra and can sing it, you can totally recuperate yourself[30]." If you feel like you are drowning in anxiety, chant this from the Heart Center and experience yourself as the fearless warrior you are. Imagine yourself battling your personal demons with bravery, strength, and power. Visualize yourself victorious!

* Translation from *The Aquarian Teacher* by Yogi Bhajan.

PAARBRAHM KARE PRATIPAALAA:
Mantra for Self-Esteem

Paarbrahm kare pratipaalaa
Sad jeea sang rakhavaalaa
The Supreme One cherishes and nurtures me.
The Supreme One is always with me and is
the protector of my Soul.

This mantra is said to increase self-esteem and self-love[31]. It calls upon us to remember the presence of a Higher Power. It doesn't require you to think of God in any one particular religious way or even by any particular name. By chanting this mantra, you connect to the realization that there is in fact a power greater than ourselves that governs things and that this same power cherishes us and is with us even in the darkest moments of our life. If we are worthy of the notice of that kind of power, worthy of the love and protection of some greater force, whatever that presence is called (God, Angels, the Universe, Light), then we are worthy of loving ourselves, protecting ourselves, and nurturing ourselves. By allowing the energy of this mantra to inspire us, we wake up to our own worth.

RAKHAY RAKHANHAAR:
Mantra for Protection from Negative Forces

Rakhay rakhanhaar aap ubaarian
Gur kee pairee paa-eh kaaj savaarian
Hoaa aap dayaal manho na visaarian
Saadh janaa kai sang bhavajal taarian
Saakat nindak dusht khin maa-eh bidaarian
Tis saahib kee tayk naanak manai maa-eh
Jis simarat sukh ho-eh sagalay dookh jaa-eh
God Himself is looking out for us,
gives us the light, and takes care of our affairs.
God is merciful, and never forgets us.
God guides us, giving us good people to help us.
God does not allow hurt to come to us.
I take comfort in the thought of God.
When I remember God, I feel peaceful and
*happy and all my pain departs.**

There are many mantras for protection in the Kundalini Yoga tradition, but each has a slightly different energy behind it. *Rakhay Rakhanhaar* is one of these powerful mantras. Yogi Bhajan said that this shabad (holy song) would protect you from all negative forces, both inner and outer[32]. It is a powerful vibration that cuts through opposing vibrations, words, thoughts, and deeds.

This mantra also infuses the chanter and the space around them with energy, so it is especially useful if one has limited physical energy and limited wealth. It is often called a victory song, one that does away with the obstacles to fulfilling your highest destiny and calms fluctuations in the mind.

---

* Translation from *The Aquarian Teacher* by Yogi Bhajan.

SIRI SIMRITI:
Mantra for Overcoming Sexual Abuse and Trauma

Siri Simriti, Siri Bhagvati, Siri Akal, Waheguru,
Aad Hari, Anaad Hari, Siri Hari, Waheguru
Waheguru, Waheguru, Waheguru, Wahejio
Great meditation, Great primal power, Great Undying, Wondrous!
The experience of Infinite Creativity, Great Creativity, Wondrous!
The experience of the Infinite guided by the Teacher Within.*

According to the National Eating Disorders Association, it is estimated that between 30-60% of people with Eating Disorders are also victims of physical or sexual abuse or sexual trauma, including rape. For many, eating disorders develop as a way to repress, manage, or protect from further trauma. For those who have been through rape or sexual abuse, self-love becomes a very difficult thing. Your relationship with your body becomes complex and evolving. As a rape survivor, it's something I deeply understand on a personal level. Although my eating disorders began before my sexual trauma, it's hard to describe in a few sentences the impact it had on how I saw myself. Being beautiful and physically attractive became for me simultaneously terrifying and necessary, both a dangerous thing and an urgent thing, and my problems escalated significantly.

Yogi Bhajan shared this mantra as a way of restoring what has been lost to someone who has undergone intense sexual trauma[33]. It's a way of singing a self-love song back into your Body Temple. Whether you have unresolved trauma, grief, anger, fear, sadness, or any other emotion, all of which are perfectly natural, this mantra can soothe the spots within you that are torn. If you feel broken, pour this healing balm into your wounds. You are a precious, perfect creation. If you were ever told you were less than perfect, or touched in a way that made you feel less than perfect, less than beautiful, or less than respected, you deserve to heal. I know what that feels like, and you can reclaim your power. Let this mantra help you release, in a loving way, anything from your Body Temple that you don't want anymore.

---

* Translation from Spirit Voyage's *Mantrapedia*.

ANT NA SIPHATI:
Mantra for Clearing Family Karma

Ant na siphati kehn na ant
Ant na karnai dayn na ant
Ant na vaykhan sunan na ant
Ant na jaapai kiaa man mant
Ant na jaapai keetaa aakaar
Ant na jaapai paaraavaar
Ant kaaran kaytay bilalaa-he
Taa kay ant na paa-ay jaa-ay
Ayho ant na jaanai ko-i
Bahutaa keheeai Bahutaa ho-i
Vadaa saahib oochaa thaao
Oochay oopar oochaa naao
Ayvad oochaa hovai ko-i
Tis oochay kau jaanai so-i
Jayvad aap jaanai aap aap
Naanak nadaree karamee daat
Limitless his praises,
limitless those who speak them,
Limitless his workings and his gifts.
Endless are the sounds and sights,
Limitless the mysteries of his mind.
Endless the creation,
it's expanse, here and beyond.
Countless struggle to find his limit;
it cannot be found.
Nobody knows the end;
the more is said, the more to say.
Great is the Creator, high his abode.
His Name the highest of the high.
One must gain those heights to know,
He himself knows how vast he is,
O Nanak, It is his gracious glance that
can raise a man so high.

If there are family patterns that are playing themselves out in your lack of self-esteem or in your disordered eating, you may be deeply affected by your family's karma. Codes within our cells are written by our family's history and determine more than just what we look like or to what diseases we are genetically vulnerable. These codes of happiness or distress are both taught as a child and encoded within the genes of our ancestors. Even when we are vastly different from the rest of our family, certain tendencies from childhood, toward discontent or misfortune, can be present in our unconscious and subconscious.

Even if no one else in your family suffers from low self-esteem or issues surrounding their body or food, you may feel the burden of their expectations on you. Family dramas and expectations can create enormous pressure on people, especially in their childhood and teen years, to live up to something that may not feel natural for them, contributing to feeling dissociated from the body and acting out in unhealthy ways.

Other types of family trauma, such as emotional or physical abuse, often repeat as a cycle for many generations, until someone breaks the pattern. This mantra breaks family karma and helps you step up and be the person that clears the patterns. It is said to shatter misfortune with the power of a thunderbolt and can affect generations[34].

I am powerful, strong, and wise.

CHAPTER 8

Kriyas

"When your body receives healing from you, this is the best healing."

~ Yogi Bhajan, May 9, 1995

Kriya means action that leads to manifestation, but kriya also means cleansing. Both translations work for our purposes; a kriya is an action that cleanses the mind, body, and spirit of blockages that might prevent it from manifesting its own highest potential. When the kriya calls for difficult work, extra energy is expended. When the kriya calls for rest, energy is conserved. Your whole-hearted presence within the kriya brings a state of grace and ease, even if it is difficult in the midst of things.

Practice the kriyas in this book exactly as they are written with a few modifications if necessary:

- You may reduce the times of the exercises in a kriya proportionately, but you should never go over the recommended times for safe practice.
- If you are heavily menstruating or more than 120 days pregnant, do not pump your navel or practice inversions. You can visualize yourself doing these things instead.
- If you are dealing with any injuries, do not push your healing body. If you are dealing with a shoulder injury, for example, avoid the meditations or kriyas in this book that put pressure on the shoulders. Use your best judgment.

IS IT TOO ADVANCED?

Some poses are more advanced than others, and some kriyas and meditations are harder than others. This does not mean that those who can do advanced asana are more advanced human beings. If that were true, then all acrobats would be enlightened. Some people that can easily hold Wheel Pose for several minutes can't curl their tongue for Sitali Pranayam. We're all working our stuff out in different ways. Competition and comparison have no place in Kundalini Yoga, which is part of why this is such an incredible tool for people who have disordered relationships to their own body. After a lifetime of external comparison and valuing the surface, this is about you going through your blocks and discovering yourself from the inside out in a positive way. Kundalini Yoga is between you and you. It doesn't matter if you can't do something when you start. Through discipline and consistency, what you can physically and mentally do will increase, and whatever your personal goals for your practice you can manifest them, but rarely does anyone begin without difficulties. You start where you are, do your best, and allow your best to be good enough. Over time, by moving gently and lovingly into your practice, you can watch yourself shift, change, and do more than you thought you could.

Before You Begin a Kriya

Before practicing a kriya, remember to tune in with the mantra, *Ong Namo Guru Dev Namo*, chanting it three times with your hands in Prayer Pose at the center of your chest.

Never use a kriya to purposefully harm your body! If an exercise is challenging, keep up as best you can. Do full times for these kriyas to the best of your ability, but don't set the intention of doing something difficult just to punish yourself. Challenging ourselves should be done from a place of elevating, not hurting, ourselves. Kundalini Yoga is a practice of self-awareness; and when we commit to radical self-love, we also commit to compassion and kindness! Practice ahimsa and non-harm, but do your best and give your all. Sometimes the kriyas will push the body to its perceived limits, but in keeping up there is a great healing.

Before beginning, take a moment to set up your yoga space. You can practice your kriyas on a yoga mat, sheepskin, or natural fiber cloth to cushion the body from the floor. If you are underweight, you may find it painful to sit or lie on the ground without a cushion. Create a gentle, comfortable practice space so that you give yourself the best yoga experience of self-care!

Over-Exercising

Many people with eating disorders use over-exercising as a form of purging fat from their bodies. During the height of my eating disorder I worked out 4 hours a day. If I weighed myself on the dreaded scale and found I was over my target, I would either continue to exercise and/or throw up to achieve a lower number. This book has been carefully designed not to be used as an over-exercising tool. Follow the times given and *do not* go over the maximum times stated. If you are extremely overweight or underweight, be careful with your body and mindful of not pushing yourself too far.

If you are suffering from a severe eating disorder or from any medical condition, make sure you clear any practices with your doctor and follow all medical advice.

Modifications

Some modifications are acceptable. If you have trouble sitting in Easy Pose (cross-legged), you can sit on your knees, or sit in a chair with your feet flat on the floor. If you cannot do a pose all the way, just do as much as you can. If you can't do a pose at all, visualize yourself in the posture instead. Go at your own pace and keep breathing throughout any practice.

Warm-ups

If you feel like your body needs to be warmed up before beginning a kriya, especially if you have been sitting at a desk all day or haven't exercised in a while, here are some gentle Kundalini warm-ups that help get the body ready for a longer kriya. One to three minutes of each will loosen you up and prepare you for a longer practice. Additionally, pranayams are an excellent warm-up.

Sufi Grind

Sit in Easy Pose and hold onto your knees. Rotate your spine in large circles from the base of your spine. Inhale as you rotate forward and exhale as you rotate backwards. Lead with your Heart Center. Reverse and rotate in the opposite direction for an equal amount of time.

Spinal Flex

Sit in Easy Pose with your hands on your ankles. Inhale and pull your Heart Center forward; exhale and push your Heart Center back. Rock your pelvis slightly in alignment with your motion to ensure a full stretch of the back. Keep your head level.

Life Nerve Stretch

Sit on the ground and stretch your legs out to the sides in a V-shape. Bend your right knee and place your right heel on your left thigh as close to the groin as you can, without straining the knee. Keeping your spine straight, bend yourself as close to the left leg as you can, leading from the Heart Center; do not collapse your head down to touch the thigh. Ideally, you will grab your left big toe with your fingers, using the index and middle finger of your left hand to lock around the back of the toe and your thumb to press on the toenail of your big toe, and your right hand to grab the sole of your left foot. If you cannot stretch this far down, simply grab as far down as you can on your calf. Inhale and exhale a few times in this position and then repeat on the opposite side.

Removing Stress from Your Body

When you have a negative relationship with your body and your self-image, you are putting stress on your body both physically and energetically. Over time, the accumulation of this negative energy, excess toxins, or systemic stress placed on the body can compromise the body's natural ability to cleanse, repair, and feel refreshed every day. Internal systems begin to break down. If you have caused self-harm to your body with destructive behaviors, here is a great kriya to begin repairing your relationship with yourself and change the dynamic of self-loathing to self-care.

This is a perfect kriya for daily maintenance to get your body healthy and functioning optimally. Used every day, it can help you release excess energy and get your circulation moving.

Kriya: Getting the Body Out of Distress

Originally taught by Yogi Bhajan: August 22, 1986

1. Sit with your legs straight out in front of you and alternately use both fists to hit the top of your thighs. This stimulates the third meridian where the liver and kidney meet. **30 seconds.**

Ramdesh's Insight: Do not hit yourself with hate or self-loathing, just pat yourself strongly to stimulate circulation.

2 Place your hands over your knees and massage around the kneecaps strongly. Your knees are on a water meridian, and the water element controls emotions. If your find yourself having headaches or feeling irritable, massaging your kneecaps can help bring you into balance. **Continue for 2 minutes.**

Ramdesh's Insight:
Feel yourself releasing energy and sending love in its place.

3 One hand-length below your knees on the outside of your calves, vigorously pound the pressure point on the muscles. This energy meridian controls metabolism. After **1 minute**, pound harder for an additional minute. **2 minutes total.**

4 Repeat Exercise 2, massaging your kneecaps for **10 seconds.**

5 Alternately pound the point at one hand-length above your knees on the inside of your thighs. This is a sex energy point and may be painful. It also relates to your pituitary gland. **Continue for 1 minute.**

6 Spreading your legs wide apart, grab the outside of your ankles, pressing the Achilles tendon. Raise and lower your torso to the ground between your legs. Keep your knees straight and move as quickly as you can. This adjusts the energy in your spine, which is vital for health and longevity. **1 ½ minutes.**

7 Cross your legs into Easy Pose and sit up with a straight spine. Make a tent with your fingertips at your heart level. Begin moving your fingertips in a circle while your wrists stay steady. This action is critically important to the efficacy of the entire kriya. This simple motion distributes energy into 72,000 nerve channels. **1 minute.**

8 Lie flat on your back with your arms down at your sides, palms down. Begin lifting your buttocks off the ground and lowering down again so that you create a bouncing motion with your hips. Feel like you are galloping like a horse. **2 minutes.**

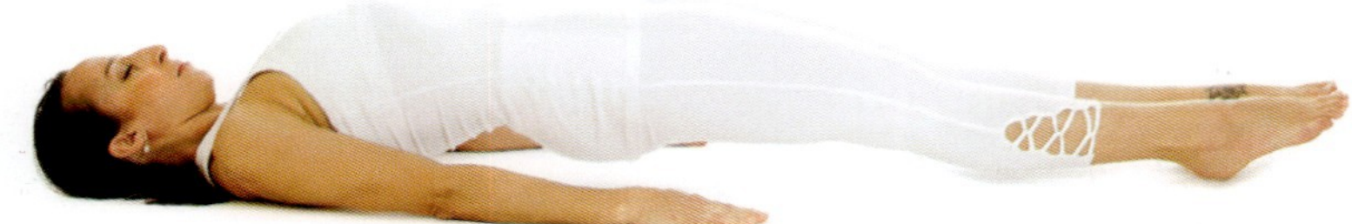

9 Lie flat on your back with your hands to your sides. Make fists with your hands, bend your elbows and hit your shoulders once, then raise your fists straight up to 90 degrees. Now quickly bring your arms back down to your sides, open your fists, and slap your palms down hard

onto the ground. Again ball your hands into fists, hit your shoulders, raise them into the air, and bring your arms down slapping your palms to the ground. Continue this motion. **1 minute.**

10 Continue lying on your back and begin hitting your shoulders with open palms. **30 seconds.**

11 Still on your back, now bring your palms to your forehead and alternately tap your palms on your forehead. **30 seconds.**

12 Bring your knees up toward your chest, extend your arms down on the inside of the knees and grab your heels, as if you are doing Chair Pose while lying on your back. Roll up and down on your spine while holding your heels. Continue for **1 minute.** Roll from the base of your spine all the way up to your neck, which will distribute energy up the spine. A flexible spine is a flexible mind. By distributing energy throughout the spine you give your body and mind the best chance to be healthy and supple.

13 Bringing your legs back down to the ground, begin to slither like a snake. Your hips and shoulders will move in opposite directions. Make your movements small and very precise. **Continue for 2 minutes.** This adjusts the vertebrae in your spine.

14 Relax and lie flat on your back. Breathe slowly and deeply from your Navel Point. Relax more and more deeply with every breath. You may listen to beautiful mantra during this relaxation, although no music is specified. **Continue for 11½ minutes.**

15 Cat Stretch slowly to the left and right. To Cat Stretch to the left, bring your right knee down to the left side of your body while stretching your right arm out to the right. To Cat Stretch to the right, bring your left knee down to the right side of your body and twist your spine as your left arm reaches out to the left. **1 minute.**

16 Lie flat again with your hands by your side, tuck in your chin, and keeping your shoulders down, lift your head and neck off the ground. Your hands remain flat on the floor by your side. Your body is relaxed, but your neck should be a bit tense. **1 minute.**

17 Relax your neck back down and close your eyes. Come sitting up into Easy Pose and assess your body and how it feels. Give yourself the opportunity to sit neutrally in your body, without shame or fear. Assess the energy that now moves throughout your entire form. **2 minutes.**

Ramdesh's Insight: Think loving thoughts and send healing energy while you touch your body.

18 Finish with this brief self-massage:

a. With your thumbs, massage under your cheek bones. **15 seconds.**

b. With the base of your palms, massage your jaw in circles. **20 seconds.**

c. Use three fingers of each hand to massage the sides of your neck. **10 seconds.**

d. Massage your ears with your palms in a circular motion. **30 seconds.**

Making Peace with Food

This next kriya allows us to experience conscious eating to retrain our bodies and minds to eat for health and repair our relationship with food. It teaches us from the inside out how to eat mindfully and digest with consciousness. It takes about 50-60 minutes to complete, can be done in a group or alone, and should be done with nourishing foods. Do not do this with junk food or trigger foods. This kriya is divided into five parts: Mental Preparation, Eating Consciously, Meditation on Digestion, Eating Unconsciously for Contrast, and Cleaning Up.

I've included the original transcript of the lecture in which Yogi Bhajan takes you through this healing kriya himself. Imagine that you are at a table with this great master of yogic science, and allow him to guide you through this powerful eating exercise. If you are in an advanced state of a serious eating disorder such as anorexia or bulimia, consult with your doctor or therapist as to whether you can safely engage in this kriya at this time. If you are healing your relationship to food and seeking to strengthen your self-image, or learning to overcome compulsive overeating or compulsive restricting, this kriya may benefit you enormously as it teaches you to eat consciously and to consider meals a spiritual practice.

Yogi Bhajan said about this kriya:

"You eat to live. You should not gobble food, because the secretion of the stomach is ordered by the pituitary and on the command of the pineal, so when you quickly fill your stomach, bloat it up immediately, and give it a shock, then it gives your body a shock for the next three hours. This is what we call an upset stomach. For food to be rejuvenating and to give strength to keep the body young, you have to use the saliva of your mouth. If you do not mix saliva in every morsel of your food, you are eating poison.

If you procedurally eat the food which you usually gulp in 15 minutes, it will become your best friend, your best strength, and your best self. Usually when you eat, your entire nervous system moves and you move your mouth and tongue together. But you just swallow things, you don't eat them. When you swallow food that is not chewed properly, it swallows your strength, your life. Then nothing is left of you. Slow eating is one of the best meditations on this Earth."

Kriya: Bhoj Kriya for Conscious Eating

Originally taught by Yogi Bhajan: August 13, 1992

Part One: MENTAL PREPARATION

Ramdesh's Insight: The instructions for Bhoj Kriya are taken verbatim from the original lecture by Yogi Bhajan in order to give you the experience of having a spiritual master guide you through a conscious eating exercise. I didn't write them myself, but instead am practicing right along with you! Imagine him speaking these powerful words directly to you to grow your self-awareness around food and eating. Enjoy this unique experience!

1. Bring the dish you like the most. Put it before you as though you are being served in a restaurant.

2. Now please sit calmly and fold your hands in Prayer Pose, and close your eyes and feel you are going to be blessed. Calm down and empty yourself to receive the gift of God. If there is no emptiness, nothing will come in. It is for your nourishment, for your acceleration, for your healing, for your purity. It is something today, at this moment, marvelously wonderful, bless-ful, blissful. Please concentrate. Bow your head in prayer a moment.

3 Please open your eyes and place your hands on your shoulders, right hand on right shoulder, left hand on left shoulder as a sign of strength. Then place your hands on your knees as a sign of strength. Then place your hands over your heart, one hand over the other as a sign of compassion. Then touch your forehead with the palms over the eyes.

4 Place your hands, palms down, over the food to bless it. Concentrate and bless your own food. Calmly and quietly make a relationship with your food and your spirit. There is God in you—feel it, feel the food piece by piece, touch it, and request of it, that when you become part of it and it becomes part of you, there is a union.

Part Two: EATING CONSCIOUSLY

5 Now please, with your hands, choose what you are going to eat. There is no spoon to be used. You have to use your hands only. When you put each morsel in your mouth, it should have the touch of all five fingers. Id—you, Jupiter, Saturn, Sun, and Mercury. Whatever little portion you have, put it in your mouth, like a kiss. Chew it totally, freely, openly. Your lips do not have to be closed. It must have 25 percent of its size mixed with saliva. Saliva is the most nurturing, health-giving, young-making stuff. It's right in your mouth. Chew it, don't swallow it.

6 Now with your tongue feel the food. If there is any hardness, keep chewing. When the food is soft, like jelly, bring it to the tip of the tongue, you will find

out that it is sweet. If it's not, keep chewing it. Food should not go to the throat or into the stomach until it is sweet to your tongue.

7 Very slowly, take it in. Then clean the inside of your mouth with your tongue, including around your teeth until there is no food left. There should be not one trace of food left in your mouth.

Now calmly and quietly, using this procedure, please eat. Keep eating and keep relating, keep meditating, keep talking to your food. Your entire mental energy should be in the food. Just imagine you are sitting in the heavens and God is serving you with food and you are nurturing yourself. Each time you take in food, you have to repeat this process.

Continue for **35 minutes**. Don't totally finish all the food because I have to show you the difference, so keep some part to eat little later.

Part Three: MEDITATION ON DIGESTING

8 The hand you used to eat with, take that hand and bring all the fingers together in a point, and put that in the palm of the other hand. Close that hand like a fist over the food hand. And feel it. Meditate. This is a healing by your own food. Your hand has touched the essence of the food. Concentrate. Continue for **3 minutes.**

Now go deeper and further inside, and digest your food. Turn it into nectar. There is a saying: "If you cannot bless your food, and cannot befriend it, you have no relationship with your own life." You have two minutes to feel light. Your food must digest by the will of your mind. Continue for **4 minutes**.

Part Four: EATING UNCONSCIOUSLY

9 Now please open your eyes and see the food you still have left. Eat the food any the old animal-like way, gobble it. You have to do that now. Become as animals, gobble it, go, go, go, go, go. Fast, unchewed, swallow. Grab it, put it in. Just see the difference. Go, go, fast, finish it, so that your body will create a resistance to this animal-like eating. There is an animal way of eating and there is a human way of eating. There is also an angelic way of eating. Angelic eating is sattvic bhoj. Continue for **4 minutes.**

Part Five: CLEANING UP

10 Now you have to get up. Go wash your hands, face, elbows, eyes, earlobes, above the eyebrows, and the back of the neck. And take the water and sprinkle it on your face.

Yogi Bhajan's Comments: *Your power is in your mind. Your body is just a vehicle. You are not eating food, you are eating for your health, your vitality, your energy, your prosperity, your strength, your "fateh"—your power to conquer. When you eat food, it is God's own self. Bhoj Kriya, done correctly, makes you healthy, mentally powerful, physically sturdy, and spiritually absolutely very beautiful and saintly . . . Your life will be long and your power will be great if you taste every morsel of the food you eat.*

Care of the Nervous System

Habits and addictions often stem from a weakened nervous system, which is then further weakened by unhealthy behaviors. If you have restricted food, overindulged in food, over-exercised, used laxatives, or induced vomiting, you have weakened your nervous system. Even a stressful, anxious life will weaken your nervous system. You may experience this as shaking hands, shortness of breath, a generalized anxiety, or an inability to calmly face the challenges of life without relapsing into unhealthy behaviors. A strong nervous system allows you to keep a level head, a calm body, and a strong mental state of mind.

Kriya: For Nervous System Overhaul

Originally taught by Yogi Bhajan: December 5, 1985

This kriya engages your Navel Center, which will help you develop the strength needed to change habits and create a healthier life. Breath of Fire, the pranayam practiced through much of the kriya, is extremely cleansing and energizing. This is a challenging kriya and it will tax your nervous system in a controlled way, which will allow it to get stronger, like working out a muscle. You may experience heat building in the body.

1. Lie on your back and breath long, slowly, and deeply through your nose for **1 minute**.

2 Still lying on your back, raise your legs one at a time to 90 degrees and crisscross them back and forth. Begin Breath of Fire. (See Pranayam section for reference.) Sync your movements to your breath. **90 seconds**.

Ramdesh's Insight: Visualize burning away those things which no longer serve your happiness.

3 Now raise your legs rapidly to 90 degrees, one at a time. Continue Breath of Fire. Keep your legs straight. **3 minutes**.

4 Repeat Exercise 2 for **30 seconds**. Move quickly!

5 Now lift both legs at the same time to 90 degrees. Continue Breath of Fire. Continue for **3 minutes**.

6 Repeat Exercise 2. Move quickly for **30 seconds**.

7 Raise both legs up to 90 degrees, grab your calves and lift your nose to your knees. Balance on your buttocks. Exhale and lower your torso back down. Then inhale and lift your head back up to your knees. Continue Breath of Fire. **2 ½ minutes**. This exercise affects your lymph and seals energy into your organs.

8 Lie on your back with your legs at 90 degrees and crisscross them rapidly for **10 seconds**.

9 Lower your legs down and relax on your back. (Yogi Bhajan played the gong during this part of the kriya.) **4 ½ minutes**.

10 Before getting up, do a few Cat Stretches to each side. Grab your right knee with your left hand and bring the knee over down to the floor next to the left side of your body, twisting your spine. Reach your right hand out on the floor perpendicular to your body and turn your head to look at your right hand. Feel a strong stretch across your body. Exhale and repeat this on the other side, stretching the opposite way.

Finding Your Inner Beauty

Too often we relate to our outer beauty as the source of our joy and happiness. This kriya helps you to relate to your inner beauty and feel your worth and value from the inside out. If you find yourself thinking that your only dream is to lose weight, be thin, or look pretty, try this kriya. If you spend a lot of time criticizing your looks and wishing your body were different, try this kriya. It will slowly teach you to practice self-love, relate to inner joy, and allow the flourishing of your spirit.

Kriya: To See the Inner Beauty

Originally taught by Yogi Bhajan: February 9, 1970

1. Sit in Easy Pose, keeping a straight spine. Bring your hands into prayer pose at the center of your chest. Apply a Neck Lock, bringing the chin slightly back and toward the chest. Bring your eyes down and focus at your thumbs. Breathe long and deeply, holding this position for **6-11 minutes** (start at 6 and build up). When your posture is correct, you may feel a tingling at your forehead. This opens your higher chakras.

2. Sit in Celibate Pose with the buttocks on the ground between your heels. (If this creates painful pressure in your knees or you cannot reach the floor, place a cushion between your heels and sit on that.) With your knees spread wide, grasp your knees and keep your elbows straight.

Rock the lower spine back and forth on the ground, so that you are gracefully vibrating your lower spine. Develop a light sweat. **Continue for 3 minutes.** Then inhale deeply and circulate the energy throughout your energetic field. This exercise should be pleasant and enjoyable. It delivers the energy stored at the base of your spine to your higher centers.

Ramdesh's Insight: It is often said that a flexible spine is a flexible mind, so to get you out of your established mental patterns, it is very helpful to increase spinal flexibility.

3 Extend your legs straight out in front of you and reach forward, grasping your toes. Relax your head down and let everything go. Merge into the sensation of infinite light. This posture helps to release tension from the spine.

4 Sit in Easy Pose and chant any mantra that makes you feel good and experience joy. No specific time was given, so chant as long as you desire.

Ramdesh's Insight: Allow yourself to feel your inner beauty and experience a deep inner peace.

Balancing Your Emotions

Many people who struggle with body image and disordered eating never learned to deal with their emotions in a healthy way. For many who struggle with binge eating, purging, or restriction, the pattern of disorder is a reaction to feelings. When you overeat, you are using food to push uncomfortable emotions down and away from you. When you purge, you are trying to remove uncomfortable sensations from the mind and body. When you restrict, you are using hunger to keep uncomfortable feelings at arm's length, in order to assert your control. It is also a tendency for some people to project what's really bothering them onto their body as if it must be their body's fault. If a relationship falls apart, you might think if you were hotter, you'd still be together, or worry that no one will find you sexually desirable again, because as uncomfortable as those thoughts are, they still feel safer than the deeper wounds of your heart.

When you feel like you can't get a handle on your anxiety, can't control your sense of self-worth, get too negative with yourself and others, and feel your body starting to lock up, it's time to balance your emotions.

Kriya: For Emotional Balance

Originally taught by Yogi Bhajan: July 21, 1977

This powerful but simple set can help keep your emotions balanced and give you a tool to reach for when anxiety or discomfort looms. You can practice it every morning to set the tone for your day, or pull it out when you find yourself becoming overly emotional or coldly distant.

1. Stand up tall with your knees and heels together. Angle your feet out 45 degrees for balance. Stretch up with your arms and bend backwards 20 degrees, allowing your head, arms, and spine to form one long, graceful arch. Keep your arms in alignment with your ears so they don't bend back too far. Palms should face forward (if you have difficulty keeping your arms up, you can hook your thumbs together for a boost). Hold this long stretch gently for **2 minutes** and use long deep breathing to settle into your body and remain calm.

Comments: Yogi Bhajan said that this exercise, known as Miracle Bend, would "bend the negativity out of the human." It balances your Navel Point, so critically important for self-esteem, brings a harmonic balance to your energy and emotions, and transforms anger into peace.

2 Gradually and slowly, bend at the waist to lower your hands to the floor, keeping your arms in line with your ears, then as you reach the end of your forward bend, allow your arms to hang toward the floor. Inhale and suspend your breath, pumping your belly in and out as long as you can. Then exhale, holding your breath out, and again pump your belly in and out as long as you can. Continue holding the breath in and pumping, and then holding the breath out and pumping at intervals. Continue for **2 minutes**. Imagine draining your tension, habits, and negative patterns of thought around your body down your spine and out your fingertips into the ground. To end, relax your breathing and slowly bring yourself into a standing position.

Ramdesh's Insight: This exercise helps to release feelings of anxiety. It allows negativity to release from your body and helps you safely release emotions.

3 In a standing position, spread your feet as wide as possible. Bend your elbows so that your forearms are parallel with the floor and your hands are relaxed at the wrists. Begin rotating your hips in large circles at a moderate pace. You may rotate your hips in either direction. Continue for **2 minutes**.

Ramdesh's Insight: Rotating your hips helps release tensions and emotions stored in the hips and lower back. Feelings of insecurity and fear often lodge in these areas of the body and can become quite tight for people who get stuck in patterns of fear. Don't judge any tightness in the body, simply encourage it to release and relax. Allow yourself to awaken the strength within you that will allow you to live a fearless life!

Ramdesh's Insight: This exercise challenges our brains with coordination and concentration, encouraging clear thinking. Break through your habitual thought patterns and allow yourself to feel more naturally comfortable within your body.

4 With your feet still in this wide stance, straighten your elbows and hold your arms straight out from the body. Begin rotating the arms at the same time in different directions. One arm will be rotating clockwise and the other counterclockwise. Your hands should be angled out away from the body 30 degrees. Do this quickly, at a speed of one full rotation per second. While rotating your arms, bend forward at a 45-degree angle and then raise yourself up and bend backward to a 45-degree angle in a constant forward and backward motion. Each full motion, backward and forward, should take approximately 15 seconds. Continue for **1 ½ minutes**. To end, stand straight and relax.

Ramdesh's Insight: You may play beautiful mantras or guided visualizations to help you relax during this time if you choose.

5 Lower yourself to the ground and relax flat on your back. Relax your arms down by your sides with your palms facing up. Relax for a full **10 minutes** to allow the effects of this yoga set to integrate.

Changing How You See Yourself

The issue with body image is that it is entirely based on perception. It's all in how we see ourselves, not in what is actually there to see. Particularly for those who experience Body Dysmorphia Disorder, their ability to see themselves accurately is hindered. If you have a negative perception of yourself, it's not going to go away when you lose some weight. In fact, I have better self-esteem and see myself as more beautiful now than I did when I was much lighter. If you had asked me how I looked at the height of my eating disorder, I would have told you that I was fat and disgusting. I would have pinched and prodded non-existent fat and barely-there lumps that for me were very real and felt incredibly important to remove, even vital. The problem was never in my body; it never has been and never could be. The problem was only and always in my perception; a personality that led me to be too critical, a nervous system that was fried from too much drink, party, and stress, and a lack of self-identification with my own spirit.

Kriya: For Personality, Nerves, and Perception

Originally taught by Yogi Bhajan: February 2, 1970

This kriya gives you patience and will take the blinders off of physical and mental vision. It also aids your liver, which can become strained by lifestyle choices, and cause you to be filled with anger and self-judgment. Let it all go and recreate your personality, nerves, and perception.

1 Sit on your heels and extend your arms straight out parallel with the ground. Lean back 30 degrees and fix your eyes on one spot without blinking (as best you can). Breathe normally and keep the body very still. **3 minutes**. Inhale deeply and relax. You may gradually increase the time of this exercise to 31 minutes. Rock pose (sitting on the knees) aids in digestion, both physically and emotionally.

Ramdesh's Insight: Those who suffer from an extreme distortion of body-image may benefit from doing this kriya every day for longer periods of time such as 40, 90, 120, or 1,000 days.

Ramdesh's Insight: Fixing your eyes on a distant point relieves eye strain in a gadget-filled world. If you spend a lot of time on the computer or mobile device, this exercise will help relieve a lot of the tension on your eyes and help you relax.

2 Sit with your knees raised to your chest. Interlace your fingers and grab your left knee with your hands. Extend your right leg up to 60 degrees, keeping your knee as straight as you can. Fix your eyes on a distant point. Breathe long and deep and keep your back straight. **2 minutes**. Inhale, hold, and relax, and switch legs and repeat on the other side for **2 minutes**. Inhale, hold, and relax, and then repeat this exercise one more time on both sides. **8 minutes total**.

3 Sit tall and extend both legs straight out in front of you. Place your hands on the ground next to your hips, point your toes, and lift yourself up off the ground. Hold your body weight on your palms and your heels. Breathe normally. **3 minutes**.

4 Still sitting with a straight spine and your legs together pointing in front of you, raise your hands above your head and touch your palms together. Stretch your hands up and hug your ears. Keep your spine straight. Imagine you are diving into heaven. Hold for **1 ½ minutes**.

5 Relax completely on your back for as long as you'd like.

Ramdesh's Insight: You might enjoy using this opportunity to play some beautiful mantra music or a guided visualization.

Balancing Your Mind

hands spread out between your feet. Keep your head facing front. Now inhale and raise your buttocks high while keeping your heels off the

on the floor. Exhale and lower your buttocks back towards the ground, lifting your head back up into the starting position. Continue lifting your buttocks up and down, keeping your hands on the floor the entire time. **108 times**. Frog Pose is a powerful antidepressant and energizer.

4 Sit in Easy Pose and relax. **11 minutes**. You can sit silently or listen to an uplifting mantra.

Ramdesh's Insight: If you have trouble with your knees, use a cushion to assist you. If you cannot lower your forehead to the floor, you can put a cushion between your legs or under brow.

5 Bring yourself onto your knees, spread your heels, and lower your buttocks onto the floor. Spread your knees as far apart as you can. Clasp your hands behind your back and begin lowering your head to the floor and raising yourself back up to vertical. As you raise and lower your head, move your shoulders up and down like a snake slithering. For **3 minutes**, let your spine dance!

6 Now lie on your back and bring your knees into your chest, locking your arms firmly around your knees. Hold this position and bounce yourself up and down off the ground as best you can. **7 minutes**.

7 Sit in Easy Pose with a straight spine and place your hands resting palms down on your knees. Inhale and powerfully exhale in one hard stroke so that the sound of the exhale sounds like *Har*, which means Infinite One. You are not chanting, but instead creating the sound of the mantra with the force of your exhale through your nostrils. Pump your navel as you exhale so that your exhale goes all the way from your Navel Center to your nose. **3-5 minutes**.

8 Relax on your back and take a refreshing nap. **8 minutes**. Yogi Bhajan played the gong during this relaxation.

9 Wake yourself up by moving around on the ground like a wriggling fish. Dance while lying down and make sure you are shaking all of your muscles. **4 minutes**.

Care of the Stomach

For those who have struggled with binge eating, bulimia, food addictions, or just plain bad diet, our behaviors catch up with our digestive systems and begin to cause havoc. Our ability to process toxins in the body slows down. Our stomach's natural balance of digestive enzymes and healthy bacteria is disrupted and eventually our systems become poisoned. If you have been abusing your stomach, your energy will be low and your systems sluggish. Our stomach is the seat of our fire in yogic teachings. It is the fire source that helps us metabolize our food, burn through negative emotions, and find the fire to achieve our goals. Yogic science teaches that the mind and the stomach are intimately related. If you do not care for your stomach, depression becomes a difficult thing to break.

One of the greatest acts of recovery is to begin consciously repairing the systems our addictions and behaviors have damaged. It's a way of seeking reparations for the body, an atonement to the Body Temple. If we have hurt our stomach, then we must clean it up, repair it, and rejuvenate it again.

Kriya: For Strengthening the Stomach

Originally taught by Yogi Bhajan: October 31, 1984

This kriya helps to restore the stomach to health. It helps your body digest more efficiently and eliminate toxins more effectively. As Yogi Bhajan said, "Anything that remains within your body for more than 24 hours will poison your body. That is the main cause of all your problems." When our stomach comes back into alignment and toxins leave our body, we begin to feel healthier and stronger. When our body, and in particular our stomach, feels healthy and strong, it's much easier to get a handle on our mental and emotional balance.

1. Lie on your back, keep your heels together, and lift both legs straight up into the air as you inhale

through the mouth. Then lower your legs to the ground while exhaling through the nose. Keep your legs straight. **3 ½ minutes.**

Ramdesh's Insight: Visualize yourself deeply healing your stomach, and allow its energy to become totally restored.

2 Sit on your heels in Rock Pose and bring your hands to your shoulders. Inhale through your mouth as you come up onto your knees and exhale through your nose as your lower yourself back into Rock Pose. Move quickly. **3 ½ minutes**. Rock Pose is a powerful asana for digestion.

3 Sit in Easy Pose with your hands on your knees and begin rotating from the stomach in powerful counter-clockwise circles. Move your lower back strongly. Imagine you are churning your stomach and cleaning you entire digestive system. **4 minutes**.

4 Staying in Easy Pose, interlace your hands behind your back. Inhale through your mouth as you lower your forehead to the floor, raising your hands up behind you, and exhale through your nose as you raise yourself back up straight and lower your arms down. Go quickly! **3 ½ minutes**. This exercise balances any imbalanced energy in the digestive system.

5 Lie flat on your back. Focus your awareness onto your Navel Point and stomach. Vibrate deeply healing, powerful energy into this point. (Yogi Bhajan played the gong during this section of the kriya; you may play a gong recording.) **8 ½ minutes.**

To End: Roll your wrists and ankles in circles. Bring your knees to your chest and rock on your spine. Stretch each of your legs out one by one a few times and relax.

Dancing Your Way to Joy

Sometimes the best thing we can do for ourselves is also the kindest and gentlest. Dancing and allowing the body to release stored tension and trauma can be a wonderful way to speed up recovery from an eating disorder or create a strong practice of self-love. For many people who struggle with self-love, being present in their bodies is the last thing they want to do. But this gentle movement relaxation makes the body a peaceful place. It allows our spirits to feel safe in our bodies again. In order to maintain a long-term relationship of kindness with ourselves and our bodies, we have to be able to stay present, feel good, and be at peace. It is one of my absolute favorite kriyas to teach in groups, especially with people who need to learn to love themselves again after experiencing trauma and abuse, or people who have been told they are ugly, worthless, or unlovable and have come to believe it. It's an incredibly freeing opportunity to redefine your relationship to your body and change the narrative of your self-worth.

Kriya: Movement Relaxation Series

Originally taught by Yogi Bhajan: August 22, 1986

This gentle dancing series gives you the chance to relax into your body and make peace with it. Call a truce, shut your eyes, and allow yourself to feel beautiful. This kriya releases the stored emotional trauma that we keep in our bodies, that build up and can turn to mental imbalances.

1. Stand up and close your eyes. Relax your arms. Become aware of your body and all of its parts. Feel any tension that is in your body and consciously let it go. Begin to sway and dance. Allow every part of your body to move. Dance gracefully, letting the movement reach every part of your body. Play high vibrational music in the background and let your heart dance along with your body. Suggested practice is **3-11 minutes**. This strengthens your heart and circulatory systems.

Ramdesh's Insight: Do not allow yourself to become shy or shameful. With the gentle touch of a divine lover, touch every square inch of your body the way you always should have been touched. Energetically place adoration and love into every part of your body as you touch it. You may feel energy buzzing from your palms; this practice smoothes the energy of the aura.

2 Remain standing and with your eyes closed, begin to move your hands over your body, touching every single part. **3-5 minutes**.

3 Lean forward from your waist and drop your arms and hands down toward the ground. Hang forward and allow all your muscles to relax. Breathe normally. **3-11 minutes**.

Ramdesh's Insight: Feel stress and pain draining out of your spine, down your hands, and into the earth.

4 Inhale and exhale deeply several times, then slowly bring yourself up straight and lean back and hang backward. Your arms should hang loosely at your sides. Breathe normally. **1 minute**.

Ramdesh's Insight: You may choose to listen to mantra or a guided visualization or relaxation.

5 Now come lying onto your back and completely relax for **10 minutes**.

Cutting the Cords

Many people experience repeated negative thinking and feel like they can't control their thoughts. If your mind is out of control and negativity has become the default, especially for those who experience things like Body Dysmorphic Disorder or chronic low self-esteem, it can be very challenging to turn the corner in your mind and develop an emotional resilience to negative thoughts. The key is to observe them but not be affected by them. For example, sometimes my mind will still default to a "you're fat" comment when I look in the mirror, but I have built an emotional resilience to these types of thoughts, and I don't identify with them when they come up. I don't latch onto it, so it doesn't cause me any pain. Over time, these thoughts come up less and less. When you don't react to the negative thoughts, they lose their power and frequency. An insult can only hurt you if you believe it's true. When you stop believing your own negative thoughts, they have no power over you. Using the technology of Kundalini Yoga to assist you in building emotional resilience to negativity and cutting the cords to your negative thoughts can be life-changing.

Kriya: For Emotional Resilience–Cutting Negative Thoughts

Originally taught by Yogi Bhajan: November 16, 1989

This kriya helps you cut the cords to your subconscious that store repeated negative thought patterns. Cutting the cords helps you establish an emotional resiliency to these thoughts and break out of your belief in them.

1. Make a V-shape with your forefinger and middle finger on both hands, pressing your ring and pinkie fingers down with your thumbs. With your elbows at your sides, raise your hands straight out from your body, palms facing each other. Begin opening and closing your fingers like scissors. After **3 minutes**, intentionally pull your most negative thoughts from your subconscious mind and scissor through them with your hands. Work as hard as you can at cutting through your worst thoughts. Continue for **11 minutes**.

2 Continuing to scissor your fingers, begin a loud Cannon Breath with a rounded mouth, breathing powerfully through your mouth. Continue for **90 seconds**.

3 Continue to scissor your fingers, create a "pa pa" sound with the movement of your lips. Don't speak the sound aloud, simple allow the popping of your lips open to create a "pa" sound. Continue bringing up negative thoughts from your subconscious and cutting them. Continue for **90 seconds**.

4 Continue to scissor your fingers and create the "pa pa" sound. Imagine that you are abusing someone with your mouth and lips. Become obnoxious, and then become abusive with your thoughts. Pull the negative, obnoxious, and abusive thoughts up to the surface where you can see and feel them and release them. Continue for **90 seconds**. Inhale deeply and relax your hands.

5 Clasp your hands behind your neck and move your elbows in and out, creating a dancing movement from the Navel Center up. Your lower body below your navel should remain a solid base, while your upper body should dance and writhe wildly and angrily. (In class, the Punjabi Drums recording was played. You can use any powerful drum recording to dance to.) Continue for **6 minutes**.

Ramdesh's Insight: Fling your negative thoughts away from you, releasing their hold on you and breaking any chains to negative thinking that bind you.

6 Inhale and immediately bring your hands and arms up overhead. Spread your fingers wide, palms facing forward and elbows straight. Begin Cannon Breath, a loud forceful breath through the mouth. **60-90 seconds**. Inhale deeply and stretch up and exhale. Inhale, stretch up, and exhale for **20 seconds.** Inhale, stretch, and repeat Cannon Breath very quickly for **15 seconds**. Exhale. Inhale and hold your breath for **20 seconds** while you stretch and pull your body up as much as you can. Exhale one final time and relax.

Ramdesh's Insight: Pull in light and radiance and joy into your body.

Finding Your Courage

Low self-esteem and a lack of self-love often keep people from achieving their highest potential. It may feel like you can't snap out of the pattern that keeps you living small and that your demons are too strong to control. This too is your ego playing games with shadows in order to keep you in a comfort zone where you don't learn and grow. The truth is that to conquer any great challenges, you must develop the heart of a warrior. Finding the courage to change your patterns changes the entire game. Rather than living small, courage to change allows all the energy that is tied up in non-productive emotions and behaviors to flood back to you and support you in creating the life you want to live. You become strong enough to fight back against the cravings and do battle with deep-seated addictions, bringing love back into your life. Be a hero. Love yourself. Love your wounds. Love your flaws. Love every bit of you. You are a warrior of light!

Kriya: Warrior's Tension Release

Originally taught by Yogi Bhajan: Summer 1985

This kriya helps you to develop the courageous heart of a warrior. Practice like a martial artist, with dedication and deliberateness. This kriya strengthens your heart and releases deep-seated stress. It will build a strong personality that can be victorious over challenges, but knows how to relax into the true you.

1. Sit in Easy Pose and place your right palm on the ground to your side, about 6 inches from your body. Raise your left arm straight out to your

side and bend your arm at the elbow, until your forearm is perpendicular with the ground. Your left palm faces towards your head.

In this position, slap the ground firmly with your right hand 8 times chanting **Har** each time you hit the ground. Then begin to sharply pull in your left palm 8 times as if you were slapping your cheek, but keep your palm an inch away from your face and do not make contact, while chanting **Hari** on each pull. This motion should be very strong. Continue alternating between each hand and chant for **3 minutes**.

Ramdesh's Insight: *Har* means the creative seed potential of the Infinite and *Hari* is its manifestation as the Divine in creative existence. Connecting with the meaning can be very powerful.

2 Remain in Easy Pose and continue the previous sequence, but with both hands in the same motion at the same time. Begin by slapping both

hands onto the ground 8 times chanting **Har** and then nearly strike both cheeks 8 times chanting **Hari**. Continue for **5 minutes**.

3 Still in Easy Pose, make your hands into fists and extend your arms backwards and 45 degrees down. Keep your arms tight and bend at the elbows, bringing your fists sharply in as if you were going to hit your chest one hand at a time beginning with the left fist, but as with your cheeks, stop just before contact; alternate pulling your arms in at a rate of one near hit per second for **4 minutes**.

4 Lying on your back, make fists of your hands and punch the sky with both arms at the same time. Then lower your fists together and touch the sides of your sternum with your fingertips. Continue to alternate between these two movements for **4 minutes**.

Ramdesh's Insight: Feel like you can conquer anything and that your heart is strong and your vision clear.

5 Remaining on your back, continue punching the sky and touching your sternum with your fingertips alternating, but raise your heels 6 inches off the ground. Engage your Navel Center. Continue for **4 minutes.** (If you are menstruating or pregnant, do not lift your heels.) This exercise strengthens your intuitive mind.

Ramdesh's Insight: See yourself victorious over your challenges with body image and self-esteem!

6 Relax on your back and listen to beautiful, uplifting music. (Yogi Bhajan originally played *Dhan Dhan Ram Das Gur* by Sangeet Kaur.) Go into a state of deep relaxation and sleep. You may rest as long as you like.

Moving into the Higher Chakras

Imagine that your body has two triangle shapes that converge at the Heart Chakra. The lower triangle encompasses the First, Second, and Third Chakras (survival, sexuality and relationships, and will power) and the upper triangle encompasses the Fifth, Sixth, and Seventh Chakras (communication, intuition, and awareness). When the energy between the triangles is not balanced, one triangle becomes larger than the other and dominates the human experience. When the lower triangle is markedly bigger than the upper triangle (as it is in most modern humans), one is a slave to the desires of the body, including fear, sexual impulses, and hunger. It makes it difficult to develop discipline and can create personality imbalances that cause us to act from fear or a deep distrust of life. Particularly for those with anorexia or those looking to develop a strong body and a loving mind-body connection, this kriya can elevate, uplift, and transform.

Kriya: Transforming the Lower Triangle to the Higher Triangle

Originally taught by Yogi Bhajan: June 11, 1971

This is a relatively advanced kriya with challenging poses and no rest between exercises. It transforms the energy of your body from the lower to higher triangles by moving energy from the base triangle up to the higher brain structures including the pituitary and the pineal. Meditation becomes automatic. Do all exercises with enthusiasm and effort to maximize reward.

1 Camel Pose: Come sitting on the heels, placing your hands on your ankles and arching your back while lifting your Heart Center upward. Settle into the pose by lifting your hips as high as you can and slowly relax your head back. This pose may bring up feelings of vulnerability and fear, especially as you relax your neck and head back. If you cannot reach your heels, place your hands in the small of your back and arch your back as far as you can without hurting yourself. Begin Breath of Fire. On each inhale, mentally chant **Sat** and on each exhale mentally chant **Nam**. Continue for **3 minutes**. Inhale and hold your breath for **10 seconds**. As you exhale, chant **Sat** out loud and apply Mulbandh, then inhale and relax as you chant **Nam.** Continue for **3 minutes**. This posture is helping your digestion.

2 Bow your head to the ground and rest your forehead on the ground. Interlace and lock your hands in Venus Lock and rest them behind your back. Raise your feet and shins off the ground. Balance in this position and meditate on your Third Eye Point. Continue for **3 minutes**. Stimulating the forehead balances issues of your personality and brings energy up to your brain for clear thinking. If you experience pain in your knees, make sure you have a cushion below you, such as a sheepskin or folded up blanket.

3 Maintain your posture, but bring your hands down under your shoulders to support your body and extend your left leg straight back and up to 60 degrees. Begin Breath of Fire* and kick your left leg to your buttocks in coordination with your breathing. Continue for **2 minutes**, then switch legs, and continue for an additional **2 minutes**.

* For instruction on Breath of Fire, see Chapter 4, page 50.

4 Come into Celibate Pose with your buttocks on the ground between your heels (if you can't touch the ground with your buttocks, place a cushion between your knees and sit on that). Breathe long, slow, and deep. Continue for **2 minutes**. This balances your Second Chakra for sexual potency.

5 Maintaining Celibate Pose, lie back onto the ground and extend your hands straight up in front of you, palms together. (If you cannot get into this position because of tight knees, put your legs straight out together and lie flat on the ground to avoid injury.) Begin Sat Kriya* in this position, pulling your navel in as you chant **Sat** and relaxing your navel as you chant **Nam**. Continue for **3-5 minutes**. This exercise increases your sensitivity to truth and gives you radiant power.

Ramdesh's Insight:
If you experience pain during this exercise, you may be engaging in sexual activity that is causing an energetic imbalance within you. Make sure you treat your sexual activity like the sacred act it is and relax your tension before engaging in sexual intercourse.

6 Come back into Camel Pose and begin Long Deep Breathing for **2 minutes**, then Breath of Fire for **2 minutes**. Inhale, hold your breath and as you exhale, raise yourself up out of Camel Pose and lower your head onto the ground. Go ahead and sweat!

* For instruction on Sat Kriya, see page 169.

7 Place your head on the ground in Guru Pranam and extend your arms out in front of you, palms together. Your elbows should hug your ears. Continue for **3 minutes**. This is a deeply relaxing posture that is brings energy up to your upper chakras.

8 Lie down onto your back and come up into Stretch Pose. Lift your feet 6 inches off the ground, toes pointed and hands stretched out in front of you, palms facing each other. Engage your navel and lift your head off the ground, gazing at your toes. *(Do not do Stretch Pose if you are more than 120 days pregnant or heavily menstruating.)* Begin Breath of Fire. Continue for **3 minutes**. Then begin to inhale and lift your knees to your chest and exhale lowering your legs straight out in front of you on the ground. Begin long, deep breathing and continue raising and lowering your knees for **2 minutes**.

Ramdesh's Insight: Stretch Pose is a powerful practice to master the energy of your Navel Center and release excess tension in your Navel Center.

9 Raise yourself into Shoulder Stand. Place your hands at the small of your back for support, balancing your weight on your elbows. Begin Breath of Fire. Continue for **3 minutes**. *(Do not do Shoulder Stand if you are pregnant or menstruating.)* This asana is excellent for balancing prana and apana flow, helping with digestion and circulation, and releasing tension in your intestines.

10 From Shoulder Stand, lower your feet down to the ground behind your head in Plow Pose. Place your arms down onto the floor in front of you, palms down. Begin Breath of Fire for **3 minutes** and then raise up into Shoulder Stand again and do Breath of Fire for **3 minutes.**

11 Lower your legs onto the floor and come up into Stretch Pose. Begin Breath of Fire. Continue for **3 minutes**. Then begin to inhale and lift your knees to your chest and exhale lowering your legs straight out in front of you on the ground. Begin Long Deep Breathing and continue raising and lowering your knees for **2 minutes**.

12 Turn immediately onto your stomach and interlace your hands together behind your back. Lift your head and shoulders off the ground and begin Breath of Fire. Continue for **3 minutes**, then relax. This balances your aura.

13 Continue gripping your hands behind your back, but lower your chest onto the ground. Kick your buttocks with alternating legs. Continue for **3 minutes**. This is a powerful distributor of sexual energy.

14 From this position, reach back, grab your ankles, and lift yourself up into Bow Pose. Keep the Heart Center open and rock back and forth on your stomach like a rocking horse. Continue for **2-3 minutes**. This adjusts the Navel Point and also boosts your aura.

15 Lower your hands down to the ground and place your hands under your shoulders. Lift yourself up into Cobra Pose. Begin Breath of Fire for **3 minutes**, then relax. Cobra lifts your mood and decreases stress in mind and body.

16 Bring yourself up into a seated position and place the soles of your feet together. Grasp your toes with your hands and rock left and right, opening your hips and chanting: **Gobinday Mukunday Udaray Aparay Hariang Kariang Nirnamay Akamay**. (See Mantra section for full meaning.) Continue for **5-31 minutes**, putting your full heart into singing this beautiful chant of joy!

Ramdesh's Insight: This mantra will clear subconscious blocks within you and open you up to deep and powerful meditation.

Creating a Vital Body and a Positive Mind

It isn't easy for someone with low self-esteem to say they love their body and believe it. When our self-love meter is low, it's very common for us to become highly self-critical, spending a lot of time criticizing how we look and focusing on our flaws and imperfections. The body responds to negativity by feeling less vital. I remember a time when I couldn't look in the mirror and say I loved myself; I just couldn't get the words to come out of my mouth. Now I say them freely and without reservation, letting the words "I love you" lift me up into freedom from negativity. But how do you get from not being able to say you love yourself, to saying it—and meaning it? And if you don't feel good in your own body, how do you begin to feel vital again?

The answer lies in developing a strong aura and a powerful electromagnetic field. Imagine the aura as a light body that surrounds you and both repels negativity and attracts positivity to you. When it is strong, radiant, and bright, not only does your body feel better, but your mind does too. If you have a strong electromagnetic field and a radiant aura, you feel so good physically that it is much easier to repair any self-esteem issues. Loving yourself becomes a natural process that you don't have to try so hard to achieve.

Kriya: For Aura, Positivity, and Vitality

This gentle kriya is a great way to reconnect with your body in a loving way, strengthen your electromagnetic field, and boost your Positive Mind.

1. Sit in Easy Pose with a straight spine. Place your hands in Gyan Mudra on your knees and begin Breath of Fire. **Continue for 3 minutes**, then inhale and suspend your breath for a few seconds. Exhale and relax.

2 Continue sitting in Easy Pose, hold your ankles, and begin flexing your back. Inhale as you move forward and exhale as you arch back. **Continue for 3 minutes**, then inhale and suspend your breath for a few seconds. Exhale and relax.

3 Remaining in Easy Pose, rest your left hand on your left knee and press the tip of your right thumb into your navel. **Breathe long and deep for 3 minutes**. Inhale deeply, exhale fully and hold your breath out, pressing the thumb firmly into the navel for a few seconds. Inhale and relax.

4 Rest both hands on your knees and inhale as you lift your shoulders, then exhale as you lower them. **Continue for 3 minutes**. Inhale and lift both shoulders as high as you can, creating tension. Exhale and relax completely, releasing all of the built up tension.

5 Bring your arms straight in front of you, palms facing together. Inhale and swing your arms down and behind you as far as you can, palms facing out. Exhale and bring them back to the starting position in front of you. **Continue swinging your arms for 3 minutes**. With your arms behind you, inhale and hold your breath for a few seconds, then exhale and relax.

6 Sit in Easy Pose with your hands in Gyan Mudra and your eyes slightly open and focused on the tip of your nose. Breathe long and deep, mentally chanting **Waheguru**, thinking of **Wahe** on the inhale and **Guru** on the exhale. **Continue for 3 minutes**. Inhale deeply, hold your breath for a few seconds, exhale and relax.

Achieve Lasting Transformation

When I was just finishing my Kundalini Yoga teacher training, I requested a private meeting with my teacher trainer. I talked through some of my life story and asked her for a practice that would keep me where I wanted to be and get me where I needed to go. I thought she'd give me something extremely difficult, like a 2½ hour meditation or 1,000 days of Bound Lotus, but instead she said, quite casually, "Do 11 minutes of Sat Kriya." Surprised it wasn't longer, I said, "Only 11?" And she responded, "What, you need it to hurt more? Just do 11 minutes of Sat Kriya. It's all you need." I realized that all my years of bulimia and anorexia and self-harm had been based on the idea that for something to really work, it had to hurt. Now, 11 minutes of Sat Kriya isn't easy. It's hard work, but it's not self-torture. If you practice it for a period of 40 days, by the end of the first week or so, the physical aspect gets much easier. Sometimes the challenge is mental and sometimes it's physical, but it is doable, and it may be all you need. For anorexics and those who want to disappear, this is a particularly transformational practice. It's grounding and engages the Navel Center—the will to live center—like almost nothing else. It's one of the most important and essential kriyas in all of Kundalini Yoga. It's a complete system of health and balance. It works on all of your aspects, known and unknown.

Kriya: Sat Kriya

Sat Kriya is an essential part of a Kundalini Yoga practice. It is a complete kriya in itself. It works on every level and part of you. This practice balances your chakras, generates heat in your Navel Center, and opens your energy meridians. This kriya is grounding and elevating, and is very effective in helping one get over fears (i.e., fear of being judged, fear of gaining weight, fear of being alone). It calms the nervous system, balances your emotions, and evens out your sexual centers. It's an all-over tonic that you can start small and build up over time.

1 Sit on your heels in Rock Pose.

2 Keeping your elbows straight, raise your arms over the head, hugging your ears, and clasp your hands together (men cross right thumb over left, women cross left thumb over right). Extend both index fingers straight up like an antenna. Keep your spine still and straight. Apply a slight Neck Lock.

3 Chant **Sat Nam** in a consistent rhythm of about 8 times per 10 seconds. Chant **Sat** as you pull the navel in and up toward the spine, focusing mentally on the Navel Center. As you chant **Nam**, relax your belly and focus either at the Navel Point or at the Brow Point. **Sat Nam** should rhyme with "But Mom!" This consistent contraction and relaxation creates waves of energy that circulate throughout the body and cause balancing and healing. Continue **3-31 minutes.**

4 To end, inhale and gently squeeze the muscles all the way up your spine. Hold your breath briefly and concentrate on the area just above your Crown Chakra. Then exhale completely. Inhale, exhale totally, and then hold the breath out as you apply a firm Mahabandha—squeeze your lower pelvis, lift your diaphragm, tuck in your chin, and contract all of your spinal muscles. Hold the breath out for **5 to 20 seconds** according to your ability. Inhale and exhale.

5 Relax flat on your back for twice as long as you practiced the kriya. You may listen to inspiring mantra, follow a guided meditation, or simply relax.

Gathering in a Healing Circle

Whether you are self-conscious about your body or have an eating disorder, it can be a very isolating feeling that makes you want to hide away from others. Many people are afraid of being outed for having low self-esteem, even if they may be very gregarious and seem popular and successful. The truth is that we are all in this together, and most women, indeed most people, have felt a measure of discomfort with themselves and their bodies. Sitting in a group and using the power of group consciousness can accelerate the healing process. Yogi Bhajan said, "Recognize the other person is you." Whether you are actively seeking healing or holding space for someone else's healing, you are being healed. This kriya calls upon the Light to fill our Body Temples and restore grace, light, and joy to our physical, mental, and emotional selves. By practicing in a group, the Light floods in like a waterfall!

Kriya: Healing, Mental Beaming, and Delight

Originally taught by Yogi Bhajan: June 24, 1999

This practice is ideal for a group ready to create deep bonds of support, trust, and healing. It can also be done in pairs with a partner, or practiced individually. This kriya uses projection and sacred geometry to bring deep pranic healing and delight to those who practice it. It can be used in yoga classes to support self-love or healing from eating disorders. It could also be used in a support group as a group activity to raise consciousness.

This kriya also affects the sushmuna, which is the central column along the spine through which prana flows. When you consciously move prana through your chakras along the sushmuna, you are building up your aura, also called the Eighth Chakra by Yogi Bhajan.

Although an even number of participants is ideal (here we show how to do the practice for eight people), you can do it with more (simply increase the number in the center and the number on the perimeter).

Before You Begin: Gather a group of eight or more people. Have two pairs of people sit in Easy Pose in the center while four others sit around them in the four corners around them.

Perimeter Group: Those holding the energy of the perimeter will sit meditatively (Easy Pose or Rock Pose are fine). They will hold a strong energy of focus on their straight spine and connect with the higher Self. Those on the perimeter have closed eyes.

Ramdesh's Insight: If you don't know how to feel your energy come to neutral, tell yourself that your energy is stabilizing to neutral.

Central Group: Those people who are in the center will interlace their hands with their partners, palms touching. They should keep a strong straight spine, but keep the elbows relaxed so that hands are held between the solar plexus and the heart. Partners in the center should keep their eyes open and fix their gaze into their partner's eyes, trying not to blink. Focus on feeling the central line of energy in your body and stabilize your energy to neutral.

Both Groups: Everyone in the room now begins to consciously create one thought and beam it out around them: "Heal Me." Visualize your spine becoming a powerful rod of light. Feel your spine stretch as if you could reach into the heavens. Expand your light. Sense light, feel light, be light, and think over and over, "Heal Me. Heal Me. Heal Me." Let the Infinite come and heal you. Let light bring energy into every cell of your body, every chamber of your heart, every corner of your mind. Feel your spine become open, turn into pure light, and feel yourself becoming healed and whole. Experience delight and joy at the fullness of your consciousness. Become humble and open. Feel your devotion and love of the Infinite Consciousness in you and beyond you. Surrender your push to heal and ask to receive healing. Feel healing flow down your spine as you relax deeply. Breathe deeply and slowly, allowing each breath to purify you and cleanse anything within you that no longer serves your highest good. Feel healing light energy moving up and down your spine, energizing you, healing you, and transforming you. Fill your mind with thoughts of joy, healing, and light. Become completely balanced and open to your inner light. Continue for **11 minutes**.

To End: Inhale and exhale. Those with closed eyes should now open them; those with open eyes should now close them. Inhale and suspend your breath and contract the muscles of the anus, sex organs, and Navel Center. Feel energy rushing up your spine, lifting you nearly out of your seat. Feel energy going into every cell of your body. Exhale powerfully through your mouth. Inhale again and suspend the breath. Feel your energy flowing in and out around you without limit. Exhale out your mouth like a cannon. Everyone should now have their eyes closed. Inhale one final time and tighten your spine, feeling energy flow from your spine to your cells and back, then from your spine to the Infinite Light and back again. Become a flow of light in all directions around you. Feel your center filled with delight, filled with life, filled with bright light. Exhale and relax.

Switch Positions: People in the center should move to the perimeter and those on the perimeter should move to the center. Repeat the exercise again in new roles. Continue for **11 minutes**. After this second round of the kriya, share your experiences together as a group and reflect on how you felt.

I am at ease in my body.

CHAPTER 9

Meditations

"As long as the mind is dark and does not let the light of the soul shine in your life, you will never have the joy and success that is your birthright as a human."

~ Yogi Bhajan, January 24, 1990

Meditation is a way of training the mind to make it your friend and supporter. It's a way of focusing your thoughts to bring peace into your life, mind, and body. It is also a tool to help overcome depression and anxiety and has positive impacts on many physical systems like the nervous, endocrine, and circulatory systems.

For best results in meditation, your spine should be straight and you should apply a slight Neck Lock. Sit on something that is comfortable and that helps keep your spine straight. If you are experiencing pain in your low back, legs, hips, or ankles, find a stiff cushion to sit on; it will relieve pressure. Sitting on a sheepskin or mat made of wool, cotton, or silk is best. If you feel tight, try doing physical activity such as a kriya or warm-up before you begin meditating in order to loosen up your body that might distract your focus. You can't meditate if your body is in pain, and for many people, especially those who are underweight, sitting still can be quite painful. Use pillows to cushion your knees and hips if necessary, and a pad under your buttocks so that your sit bones don't ache. A comfortable body makes it easier to still the mind, but know that it will get easier and more comfortable to meditate as you become more experienced.

You may think that you cannot meditate, but it's not true. Perhaps you're not good at meditation yet, but we are all born with the capacity to meditate. Try this: place your right index finger on your left wrist and feel your pulse. Shut your eyes and inhale deeply and exhale, concentrating on your pulse. Inhale and exhale again and open your eyes. You can meditate. You just did!

PRACTICE MAKES YOU PERFECTLY YOU

Meditation can be challenging when you first begin; you may choose to reduce the times listed in the meditations in this chapter and build up your endurance slowly, over time. You're not failing, you're training. You can't expect to go to the gym and lift the heaviest weight with no preparation. You don't yell at yourself if you can't bench press 200 pounds on your first visit to the gym. Neither should you feel defeated if you can't meditate for 31 minutes when you first sit down. If you fidget, so what? You can't fail at this. Simply continue and allow yourself to gradually learn to fidget less. If you don't resist meditation, then you meditate much more easily. You are not going to sit down for the first time and have a clear mind and not think of anything other than the meditative focus. It won't happen. Thoughts will come up—you might think your back hurts or you have to do laundry, whatever it is—but the trick is to not follow the thoughts down the rabbit hole. When you find yourself actively thinking, simply release the thought and go back to being the observer rather than the thinker. The observer just holds space during the meditation practice. If you don't react to the moments when you find yourself "not meditating" while doing your practice, they will diminish. If you find silent meditations are too challenging, try one with a mantra. It can help to give your active mind something to think about. Or try one of the meditations using pranayam; you may be surprised how fast changing your breathing into segments can quiet your mind.

These meditations are tools for self-healing and self-transformation. They are a path to mastering your life. They are friends along your journey. Get to know them. They have a wisdom all their own and their own stories to tell. Pull up a seat, settle yourself into sacred space, and come talk to your soul, your best friend.

Unlocking Your Heart

To journey into self-love, your heart must open. If you have spent a lifetime giving love to others, but withholding unconditional love from yourself, it is time to open the lock of the heart and allow your infinite capacity for unconditional love to pour forth. If you have been wounded in a relationship and closed yourself off, it is time to take down the barriers to love.

An open and loving heart will allow you to deal gently with yourself and others, avoid criticism, harshness, and judgment, both to your own Body Temple and to others', which will allow a more free flow of energy to circulate throughout your body, bringing greater energy and vitality to your mind, body, and spirit.

This meditation jolts the chest cavity and generates a shock, which aids in opening the Heart Chakra. It adjusts the chest cavity and rib cage. When the diaphragm is out of alignment, it is said that you lose up to one third of your life force. If you have total command of your life force vitality, it becomes much easier to overcome obstacles, create new habits that promote self-love, and feel good in your own skin.

For this meditation to be effective, you have to put your heart into it. You must summon all the power you have and use great force to open up, and then stop your arms abruptly, in order to shock your central nervous system on each chant of *Har*, which opens the Heart Center, the place where you keep the fire for living life.

Opening the lock of your heart will allow love and pranic life force to circulate more easily throughout your body, and will help you develop a powerful fire for living!

Meditation: To Open the Lock of Your Heart

Originally taught by Yogi Bhajan: July 22, 1996

Sit in Easy Pose with a straight spine. Bring your hands up in front of your face, palms facing toward each other. Your hands should be 6-8 inches away from your face and distant from each other. Keep your elbows bent and relaxed.

With a very fast, very powerful jerking motion, pull your hands out until there is about 36 inches between your palms and come to a sudden stop. If you stop forcefully enough, your hands, chest, shoulders, and head will lurch forward and back. The motion should resemble being hit with an electric shock. While jerking your hands, listen to a recording of *Tantric Har*. Don't chant along to the music during this meditation. On every repetition of the word **Har**, jerk your arms back with power. Focus your awareness on your chest cavity and feel the effects. Continue for **11 minutes**.

To End: Inhale and suspend your breath, while continuing the motion for **13 seconds**, then exhale. Inhale again and hold your breath for **8 seconds** while you continue the jerking motion. Exhale. Inhale deeply one last time and continue to jerk your arms for **6 seconds**. Exhale and relax.

Ramdesh's Insight: *Tantric Har* is a well-known recording of the mantra, **Har,** chanted at a pace of 1 repetition per second. **Har** means "Infinite One" and calls upon a creative primal force.

Letting Go of What Haunts You

Many of us have internalized a dangerous lie: that we do not deserve anything good and that we should be ashamed of who we are. Often because of some early event, the patterning of "not-good-enough" lodges in our subconscious, keeping us small and preventing us from building the life we want. As we age, events happen that seem to confirm this false belief over and over. We are hurt, we are shamed, or we are used in a way that shows our minds that the world isn't safe, that we aren't worthy, or that we deserve less than happiness.

For many people with body image issues, somehow our minds have wrapped around the belief that what little self-worth we have comes from our weight, and that if we drop the pursuit of thinness or some other physical ideal, we will have no worth left at all. Our minds turn those hurtful events into weapons against us. The more painful the event, the more easily our ego can use it as a trigger. When we begin to heal ourselves of shame, the ego takes its last stand by digging into the most painful events of our past, pulling them up into our consciousness, and using them to control us. In order to release our demons, we have to confront them. In order to love ourselves, we have to love all of us, and shine a light down into the dark corners where the shadows lurk. If you are haunted by an event in the past, and you punish yourself for what happened or feel you cannot heal because of what happened, practice this meditation to help you release, forgive, and allow yourself to move forward in grace and in peace.

This meditation allows you to gently release haunting thoughts or events that continue to hurt you in the present. By letting go of our stories, we let go of our reasons to remain small, remain ill, or remain critical of ourselves.

By infusing our memories with the mantra *Waheguru*, which means the ecstasy of God Consciousness, we remind ourselves consciously and subconsciously that bliss is with us all, and that we have the power to transform all our guilt and hurt and shame if we choose. While this is a physically simple practice, it may be emotionally challenging, so do this when you feel ready and are in a safe space; but more than that, practice with bravery!

Meditation: To Remove Haunting Thoughts–10 Steps to Peace

Sit comfortably and open your eyes only 1/10th of the way so a small sliver of light can be seen. Concentrate on the tip of your nose.

Throughout this 10-step healing process, silently chant the mantra Waheguru in this manner:

Wa: mentally focus on the right eye
He: mentally focus on the left eye
Guru: mentally focus on the tip of the nose

10 STEPS TO PEACE

1. Inhale, exhale, and mentally say **Waheguru**.
2. Inhale and bring to mind the encounter or incident which happened to you.
3. Exhale and mentally say **Waheguru**.
4. Inhale. Visualize and relive the actual feeling of the encounter.
5. Exhale and again mentally repeat **Waheguru**.
6. Inhale and reverse roles in the encounter you are remembering. Become the other person and experience their perspective.
7. Exhale and mentally repeat **Waheguru**.
8. Inhale. Forgive the other person and forgive yourself.
9. Exhale and mentally repeat **Waheguru**.
10. Inhale. Let go of the incident and release it into the Universe.

Ramdesh's Insight: When processing intense emotions, it is helpful to drink a lot of water. The water element governs the emotional response in the body, and making sure you are well hydrated can make emotions feel more manageable and easier to deal with.

Creating Self-Love

To create a radical change in our world, we have to make radical changes in ourselves and our lives. If every person loved themselves in a genuine and true way, many of the world's problems would end overnight. Don't confuse arrogance with love, or self-deprecation with humility. Love is a force for good, always. Self-love is a power that spreads goodness, always. For anyone who has ever said anything unkind about themselves, there is a need to consciously create self-love.

When Yogi Bhajan taught this meditation, he talked about how those who struggle with self-love are ruled by fear. Perhaps it's a fear that you aren't good enough, you aren't smart enough, or you aren't thin enough. Perhaps it's a fear of rejection or the fear of being seen. Perhaps it's a paralyzing fear of responsibility. All of our fears are as unique as snowflakes, and yet as similar as the molecular structure of the water that makes them up. It's time to practice self-love in all things, and to get there, we need to take the first step to creating more self-love in our bodies and minds.

Meditation: Creating Self-Love

Originally taught by Yogi Bhajan: April 4, 1994

"Love doesn't rule you. What rules you is fear, phenomenal fear. Through this [kriya], love can be invoked and fear can be reduced."

~ Yogi Bhajan

This first exercise is a self-blessing that adjusts the electromagnetic field around your body and self-hypnotizes you to receive your own blessing when you may be in resistance to the idea of loving yourself. If you are filled with anger, this meditation may hurt. After about 5 minutes, this practice may also hurt if your diet is poor, so use it as a way of touching base on how healthy your food choices are.

This practice will support you in deepening into self-love and change you into a revolutionary for love. As you bless yourself, you bless the entire world.

To Practice: Please note that there are no breaks between parts. Inhale and move straight from one into the next.

Part One

Sit in Easy Pose with a straight spine and bring the left hand up, bending the left arm at the elbow, palm facing forward as if you are taking an oath. Your right hand should arc over your head, palm facing down 6-9 inches above the top of your head. Give yourself a blessing from your right palm. Allow this blessing to correct your aura. From your left palm, your blessing should spread out to the entire world. Keep your eyes closed and focused down toward the center of the chin. This eye focus is very calming and allows you to become introspective. Do your best to breathe only once per minute by inhaling for 20 seconds, holding the breath for 20 seconds, and exhaling for 20 seconds, all through the nose. It may be necessary to build up to this. Continue for **11 minutes**.

Part Two

Extend your arms straight out in front of you parallel with the ground, palms facing down. Stretch your arms as far as you can. Keep your eyes focused on the center of your chin and continue to breathe long and slow. **3 minutes**.

Part Three

Stretch your arms straight up, palms facing forward, as high as you can. Continue the same breathing and eye focus as in Part Two. **3 minutes**.

To End: Inhale and hold your breath for 10 seconds while you stretch up as high as you can and tighten all the muscles in your body. Exhale. Repeat inhale-hold-tighten-exhale sequence two more times.

Ramdesh's Insight: This exercise energizes the heart meridian and opens your Heart Center.

Overcoming Compulsive, Binge, and Emotional Eating

Overeating and emotional eating are ways that we sabotage our connection to our own life force. They are self-punishing behaviors that we develop in order to push our emotions away, but we end up pushing our spirit away, too. Overeating is one of the hardest things we can do to our bodies long term, and addictions like binge eating and bulimia wreak havoc on our bodies for many reasons. When we overeat, our bodies lose the ability to digest and the food putrefies and becomes toxic in our systems. When our bodies are toxic, our minds become toxic, and we cannot meditate peacefully or keep our emotions calm.

I know firsthand how painful compulsive overeating can be. Physically it is draining and painful, emotionally it's easy to feel like a failure and be ashamed, and mentally it's exhausting. It's also an incredibly challenging addiction to overcome. Unlike addictions that involve a substance like alcohol, which you can abstain from, when you have a disorder like binge eating you cannot abstain entirely from food. You can't just cold turkey the substance you use to fuel your addiction, and so you are tested over and over with each bite.

Yogi Bhajan explained that eating compulsively was governed by an imbalance in a specific part of the brain. He said, "Compulsive eating, irrational eating, and uncontrolled eating are self-depriving factors in the eastern hemisphere of the brain."

There is a pranayam, or breathing exercise, that can train the left hemisphere of the brain not to overreact to food and cause us to overeat. It will require will power to do it, and if your addiction to food is deep, you'll need to continue for at least 90 days. But if you have ever felt like your addiction to food is out of control and nothing helps, this is for you. Even if you don't have a compulsive overeating problem, try it for the calming effect it will have on your mind and body.

You may still relapse from time to time. Please don't shame yourself. Just keep going, keep breathing, and keep healing. Be gentle with yourself and allow healing to be as gradual as it needs to be. You can get better, and this pranayama can help.

Meditation: Pranayam to Restrain Compulsive Eating

Originally taught by Yogi Bhajan: Summer 1979

Sit in Easy Pose and block your right nostril with your right thumb. Inhale as deeply as you can through the left nostril. Hold your breath in as long as you can. Now exhale through your left nostril and hold your breath out for the same length of time as you held it in. Continue for **31 minutes**.

About this meditation, Yogi Bhajan said, "Ninety days of practicing this breath technique for 31 minutes per day can take care of most chronic cases. But don't exaggerate. It should be long, deep breathing through the left nostril without pressure on the diaphragm. It makes the initial hemisphere of the left side of the brain to take command and project itself against the impulse that 'I must go and eat.'"

Ramdesh's Insight:

I like to use a beautiful piece of mantra music that lasts for 31 minutes. If you choose to play mantra in the background, as you are breathing allow yourself to get lost in the music. It will serve as your timer, and also encourage you to keep going. If this feels like a long time to meditate, and you feel like giving up, reframe it. Meditating for 31 minutes is much easier than dealing with a binge eating disorder, compulsive overeating, or food addiction. It's much easier than feeling uncomfortable in your body all the time. Do your best, work up to the optimal time if you need to, and give yourself a chance to experience this healing.

Balancing Behavior and Impulse

Often patterns in our bodies and in our minds get stuck on replay. Especially when we are first beginning a serious spiritual practice and starting to heal, we can be surprised and discouraged when disordered behaviors pop back up. It might even discourage you to the point that you want to let go of all the progress you've made and retreat into old patterns. Don't let it! Often these residual behaviors pop up because of impulse. Our minds may be conditioned to say something critical of how we look, or our hands may be conditioned to attempt to purge after a meal, and impulse can take over; it's then we find ourselves acting out old, unhealthy patterns. You aren't a failure, and when this happens, it's important to retrain the brain not to act on impulse, but to choose conscious, graceful, self-loving behaviors. Every challenge is a learning tool. This meditation is like telling our brains, "Hey! We're not operating on that old program anymore. Thanks for trying to help, but this is the new system we're running. Update the software please!"

Meditation: For Balancing Behavior and Impulse

Originally taught by Yogi Bhajan: February 12, 1977

Yogi Bhajan said this meditation balanced energy flow and allowed us to act less impulsively and more appropriately.

Part One

Sit in Easy Pose with a straight spine. Place your hands level with your mouth, cupping your hands but keeping your fingers straight. Bend your right wrist so that your right fingers point down, while the left fingers point up. Keep your hands separated so they don't touch. Close your eyes, but mentally look through your forehead. Continue for **11 minutes**.

Part Two

Continue with the posture and eye focus, but reverse your hands so that the left fingers are pointing down and the right fingers are pointing up. Continue for **11 minutes.**

Moving Through Your Anger

Anger is one of the most physically toxic emotions, and it is difficult for anyone to feel comfortable in a body where anger resides. One of my friends who is recovering from anorexia had her condition begin after walking in on her husband cheating. Her rage at the betrayal and hurt turned inward and shut down her body's normal functioning; she simply stopped eating and any food she took in hurt her stomach. This developed into a long battle with anorexia, which included abdominal surgery and hospitalization, but it began from an anger that she internalized and could not move through in a healthy way. So many people who have trouble accepting their body have deep issues with anger. I remember screaming "I hate you!" at my body when I looked in the mirror, spitting with rage. Today, I can't even imagine saying those things to myself or feeling that way. This meditation is a powerful process to clear the anger out of your body, whether it is directed at you or at another person. Sometimes, healing your relationship with your body can be as difficult, or as easy, as releasing the uncomfortable emotions that lurk inside.

This meditation moves anger through your body so you can release it. It's a wonderful choice when you are obsessing about your anger over something and can't get yourself to stop thinking about it. Instead of trying ***not*** to think about what makes you angry, rather ***focus*** on what makes you angry using this strong breathing exercise, mudra, and movement to get it out of your body and energy field. This mudra helps to recreate your entire psyche and command all the tattvas, or elements, within your body. This practice clears the Arc Line, a halo between ear lobe to ear lobe on men and women, and also across the chest in women, a place that stores energetic imprints, including those from past relationships. A powerful Arc Line builds intuition and helps create a strong positive projection.

Meditation: Fists of Anger

Originally taught by Yogi Bhajan: January 3, 1996

Sit in Easy Pose with a straight spine with a light Neck Lock. Touch each thumb to the base of your Mercury (pinky) fingers. Close the rest of the fingers over the thumbs to form fists. Raise your arms and begin powerful alternating movements over your head, swinging up, over to make large circles. Form an "O" shape with your mouth and breathe in strong, rhythmic breaths that coordinate with your arm movements. Get mad! Think about anything and everything that makes you angry. Keep a laser focus on your rage and bring up as much anger as you can throughout this meditation, increasing the intensity of your meditation with the intensity of the anger. Eat up your anger! Move hard! Bring more prana, a life-giving energy, into your body! Continue for **3 minutes**.

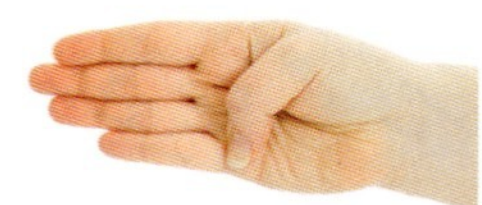

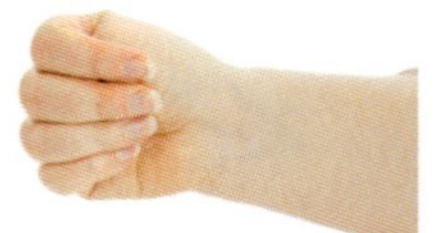

To End: Stretch the arms up overhead, interlock your fingers with palms facing up, and deeply inhale through an "O"-shaped mouth. Hold your breath for 10 seconds and stretch up as high as you can, then exhale through an "O"-shaped mouth like a cannon. Repeat 3 times. Relax. Visualize yourself surrounded in a brilliant white, healing light.

Conquer Your Inner Anger

Anger is a powerful trigger for food addictions, eating disorders, and low self-esteem. Its such a common trigger of self-destructive behavior (in fact, anger itself is self-destructive to the body) that I decided to include this second meditation devoted to the removal of stored anger from the body. This is one of the most powerful meditations I know; the first time I did it for the full 11 minutes, I was crying and sweating by the end of it. I felt anger pouring out of me in waves. I didn't feel the need to know what I was angry about, all I focused on was letting it go and keeping up with this very difficult meditation, because I could feel it working so intensely and wanted the full impact. For many who have experienced abuse at the hands of family, friends, partners, or strangers, anger will be stored in parts of the body and psyche. Perhaps you grew up in a household with anger and yelling between your parents; that too could become stored in your body. At a young age, anger can make a powerful impression, so you may find in the exploration of this practice that much of the anger you have is generational and not even your own. For others, their own anger sits on a hair trigger: the littlest things can set you off and give your addictions a reason to barge in. You may find yourself stressed at work because of something someone said, you become angry inside, and the second you get home you go straight to your fridge and overeat. You don't have to go into your story to get benefit from a practice like this. Just give yourself 11 minutes a day to sit on your yoga mat and practice this. See what kind of experiences you have and changes you feel within you. With extended practice, it will release the hair-trigger reactions and ensure that your stored anger is released from your Body Temple.

Meditation: Conquer Inner Anger and Burn It Out

Originally taught by Yogi Bhajan: March 8, 1999

If you do this practice for 11 minutes a day, your entire life will change. After 40 days, it can shift your personality dramatically.

Sit in Easy Pose with your arms stretched out straight to the sides with no bend in your elbows. Point your index fingers upwards and use your thumbs to lock down your other fingers. Your index fingers should be locked, stiff, and straight. Close your eyes and concentrate on your spine. Inhale through a rolled tongue (Sitali Pranayam) and exhale through your nose. Continue for **11 minutes**.

To End: Inhale deeply and hold your breath for 10 seconds. Stretch your arms out to the side as far as you can and then exhale. Repeat this sequence 2 more times.

Restoring Glandular Health

The glandular system is the gateway to physical health. This key system regulates hormones, digestion, metabolism, sleep, regeneration, and many other critical functions of the body. The glandular system includes the following major glands that regulate how we feel, how we manage stress, and how well our immune system functions.

Meet the glandular system:

Pituitary gland — Master gland, regulates the other glands
Adrenal gland — Produces aldosterone, cortisol, and other steroids
Hypothalamus — Mediates between the nervous system and endocrine system
Thymus — Develops immune system and produces t-cells
Parathyroid — Helps control metabolism
Thyroid — Regulates metabolism by producing thyroxine which controls the metabolic rate of cells and calcitonin for calcium levels
Pancreas — Creates insulin and stimulates glucose to go to cells
Reproductive organs — Manages fertility

Almost everyone puts stress on their body and taxes their adrenals, but people with anorexia can struggle especially with thyroid health. When your glandular system isn't strong, you are prone to illness, weakness, exhaustion, and malaise. Supporting your adrenal glands and restoring them to health is important for anyone who has abused their body over a long stretch of time, whether with an eating disorder or simply by drinking caffeine for many years.

Meditation: 16-Stroke Breath to Rebuild Your Health

Originally taught by Yogi Bhajan: September 3, 1979

This kriya can totally rebuild your glandular system; it also rids the body of toxins and rebuilds damaged cells.

Sit in Easy Pose with a straight spine and interlace the hands together with thumbs resting side by side in Venus Lock. Your thumbs do not cross. Hold the mudra at the level of your heart and rest your elbows down by your sides.

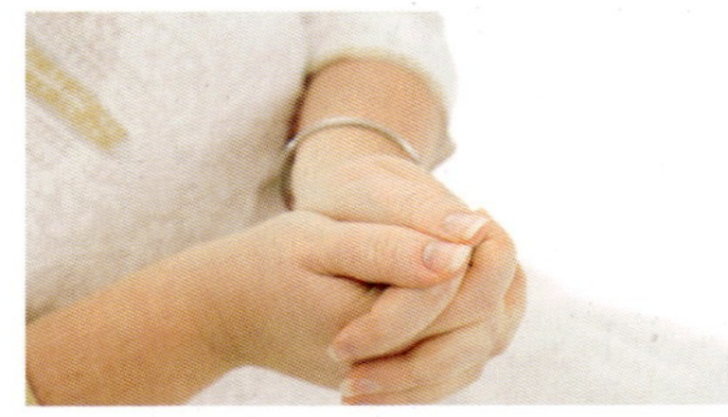

Inhale through the nose in 16 rapid, equal strokes. On each stroke, mentally vibrate, **Sa Ta Na Ma, Sa Ta Na Ma, Sa Ta Na Ma, Sa Ta Na Ma**. One full inhalation cycle should take about 6 seconds.

Start by doing **3-5 minutes**, then work up to **11 minutes**. Maximum time for this pranayam is **31 minutes**.

Overcoming Harmful Impulses

If you have a pattern of self-harm, you may have a challenge disrupting your habitual harmful impulses. It might be compulsive for you to be cruel to yourself and/or to punish yourself. You can disrupt these habits and go past the patterns of thoughts that cause self-harm. If you are harming yourself, try this meditation. This mantra encourages you to move beyond your thoughts, even beyond your body, and into the loving presence of spirit.

Meditation: To Treat Impulsive Behavior*

This meditation restores your ability to remain stable and secure and helps develop increased restraint. It balances the earth and ether elements, which are the material and immaterial aspects of you.

Part One

Sit in Easy Pose and extend your hands straight out in front of you parallel to the ground. Your left palm should face the ground and your right palm should face the sky. Close your eyes and chant **Waheguru Waheguru Waheguru Wahejio**, at least one time per breath. Continue for a maximum of **18 minutes**.

* This meditation is sourced from David Shannahoff-Khalsa, MD's *Kundalini Yoga: Meditation for Complex Psychiatric Disorders* and could not be verified by the Kundalini Research Institute.

Part Two

Bring your hands to your chest, right over left, at the Heart Center. Whisper the mantra, **Waheguru Waheguru Waheguru Wahejio**, for **2 minutes**. Then stop chanting and remain silent with your hands on your heart.

To End: Inhale and suspend the breath. Contract all the muscles of your arms, hands, and back and exhale out powerfully through the mouth making the sound of a cannon. Repeat inhale, tightening and exhaling like a cannon two more times.

Recovering from Addiction

This meditation is a critical pillar to releasing any long-term patterns of habituation, whether it's anorexia, bulimia, or simply obsessing with your weight and food. I remember during my bulimic years that I felt a very strong addiction to the release of hormones after I would purge. The adrenaline would excite me, and by giving in to my addiction, an instant type of relaxation would come to me after a long build-up. But this type of excitement and relaxation always had incredibly intense side effects: pain, depression, illness, low energy, and guilt, just to name a few. No matter how high an addict's high is, the low is lower. Over time the highs cease completely and all you are left with is pain. You don't have to have a serious, life-threatening addiction to be addictive. In fact, most people are highly functional in their addictive tendencies. Do you obsess over your weight? Do you obsess over how you look? Do you obsess over food and eating? You've become addicted to the feedback loop of how you look externally or the comfort that the act of eating can provide. Perhaps you're addicted to sugar or coffee. You don't have to have a life-threatening addiction to benefit from breaking your mind's addictive cycle. From my own understanding of Yogi Bhajan's teachings, he didn't believe in separating people out based on what made them different. He wouldn't have separated people out by "anorexic" or "bulimic"; instead he may have said, you have to right the imbalance in your brain that is causing these problems for you.

Whatever addictions you do or don't have, just try this meditation and see how it can free you from a variety of habituations that no longer serve your highest good.

Meditation: For Healing Addictions

This meditation is one of the absolute best for addictive behaviors. The pressure of your thumbs against your temples activates a reflex in your brain that triggers your pineal gland and corrects an imbalance that supports addiction.

Sit with a straight spine and make your hands into fists. Press your thumbs into your temples. Lock your back molars together with a closed mouth. Focus your eyes to the point between your eyebrows, and breathe in a relaxed manner. Silently repeat the mantra, **Sa Ta Na Ma**. With each syllable, press your molars together. You will feel a movement in your temples. Continue **5-7 minutes** (gradually increase to 20 and then to 31 minutes).

To End: Inhale and suspend your breath for a few seconds, then exhale and relax.

Becoming a Self-Healer

Taking charge of our health and our lives by stepping into the role of self-healer can create miracles. When we take responsibility for our own happiness, when we finally accept that no one and nothing can make us happy other than our spirit, we can become our own healing catalyst.

Ra Ma Da Sa is a powerful healing mantra that delivers the light of the Infinite. Play it in your environment, play it while you are sleeping, chant it while you drive or prepare a meal. Decide that you are going to heal, that you deserve to heal, and that it may take time, but that you are moving forward onto the path of joy and self-awareness. Then let the meditation and mantra work for you. All you have to do is show up on the mat and put in the time. The healing powers of the Infinite can do the heavy lifting.

Meditation: Ra Ma Da Sa Meditation for Healing

Originally taught by Yogi Bhajan: Summer 1973

This meditation works at directing the healing power of the mantra, *Ra Ma Da Sa*, into our Heart Center to heal those parts within us that feel disempowered and hopeless. This is also a powerful mantra for physical healing and releasing disease.

Sit with a straight spine in Easy Pose with a light Neck Lock. Tuck your elbows comfortably against your ribs and extend your forearms out at a 45-degree angle to the body. Pull your wrists back and your palms flat and facing up throughout the meditation. Close your eyes.

1. Chant the mantra **Ra Ma Da Sa Sa Say So Hung**. On the first **Sa** and on **Hung**, pull in your Navel Point powerfully. The **Hung** should not be long and drawn out, but clipped off forcefully as you pull in the navel. Chant one full cycle of the mantra on a single breath, then inhale and continue. As you chant this mantra, feel resonance in your mouth and sinus area, concentrating on the quality evoked by these powerful sounds.

Ra = the energy of the Sun: strong, bright, purifying

Ma = the energy of the Moon: receptive, cool, nurturing

Da = the energy of the Earth: secure, personal, action

Sa = the energy of impersonal Infinity: the cosmos in all its dimensions

Say = the energy of personal totality: the sacred Thou

So = the energy of personal merger: Identity

Hung = the energy of the vibrating, real Infinite; together, So Hung means I am Thou

As you chant this mantra, go through a circuit of the chakras. Grow towards the Infinite, link with it, and bring it down to embody it within you.

Continue chanting for 11-31 minutes.

To End: Inhale and hold your breath as you offer a healing prayer for yourself or the person you wish to bring healing to. Imagine them (or yourself) as radiant, whole, healthy, and strong. Imagine you or the other person to be completely engulfed in radiant, healing white light. Exhale and inhale again, holding your breath and offering your prayer. Exhale and then lift your arms up high and vigorously shake out your hands and fingers. Relax.

Finding the Peace Within

This is one of my favorite meditations. I keep it in my etheric tool belt to pull out when I'm panicking, stressed out, or feel like I can't communicate peacefully. We can't expect our environments to be peaceful if we're running around screaming at people and being angry with the world. We have to find the peace within. Even if the world were peaceful, you wouldn't be able to see it unless you had peace inside yourself; otherwise, it would still look chaotic. To create peace inside means to help it manifest on the outside, but it also means to be able to see the peace on the outside that is already there.

If you feel like you're constantly playing catch-up, like you're never in control of your day, like you don't say the right thing or do the right thing, and can't calm down, try this meditation. For me, it feels like rocking a baby in a cradle, except the baby is my stressed-out mind and body. After a few minutes, I'm at peace.

It will help you refine your speech, and speak gracefully to yourself and to others. Learning to master your Fifth Chakra, the Throat Center, is critical to healing many eating disorders and developing a strong practice of self-love. You have to be able to speak your truth, and to speak it gracefully in a way that does not cause pain to you or to others. A strong Subtle Body, one of the 10 Light Bodies of Kundalini Yoga, can help make that easier, and bring peace within yourself and your relationships.

Meditation: Waheguru Meditation for the Subtle Body

This hypnotic meditation is soothing and comforting, and stimulates your Subtle Body, which is a part of yogic anatomy that contains within it sophistication and refinement. You can use this practice to instantly calm yourself any time you feel disconnected from your own true grace and inner light.

Sit in Easy Pose with a straight spine. Place your hands in Gyan Mudra (thumb and forefinger touching).Turn your head to the left, bringing your chin to your left shoulder, and chant **Wahe**; then turn your head to the right, bringing your chin to your right shoulder, and chant **Guru**. Continue this motion and chanting, back and forth.

Focus your awareness on the union of the two triangles from the nose and the eyes, and the eyes and the Third Eye. Continue for **11-31 minutes**.

Conquering Upset

At some point in the journey to loving ourselves and having a peaceful relationship with food, something is going to happen that will nearly derail us. We'll get upset over some challenge or difficulty, and it is easy to fall back into our disordered eating, or our cruel self-talk, or our self-harm as a crutch. The ego is going to use upset to unhinge our healing; the second something bad happens or someone says something, the ego will try to assert itself into the mind with obnoxious self-talk to trigger us back into old patterns.

Let's say you're recovering from anorexia. You are beginning to use food to self-nourish and put on a few healthy, needed pounds. Someone who hasn't seen you and doesn't know your story says to you, "Oh you look great! You're gaining some weight!" Nothing in the sentence itself is harmful. The person may be intending to reinforce your healthy choices, but all your ego hears is "You're gaining weight" and sends you into a spiral of upset that tells you you're fat, you're gross, and you begin to panic. This happens over and over for people recovering from eating disorders. One tiny word or thought and our minds spiral back out of control, and we begin to binge and purge or skip a few meals in an attempt to "get back in control" of our minds and bodies. It's an illusion and it's not real control. In fact, it's the relinquishing of control to a negative thought form.

The key is to be prepared: know that you're going to get triggered. You have to anticipate that at some point during your healing process, upset will come to trigger you and potentially take you off your path. This meditation is the plan: use mantra to stop the path of our negative thought patterns in their tracks before they can manifest in our field and create an obstacle in our positive, healing behaviors. If our negative thoughts are like arrows, mantra is a shield that deflects the arrows before they can cause harm. By creating the sacred sound current in our meditations, through the practice of mantra, we essentially establish a force field around us that protects us from upset and keeps us on the path of love.

Meditation: To Conquer Upset

Originally taught by Yogi Bhajan: March 16, 1978

This meditation conquers our tendency to succumb to upset. It strengthens our aura and the Fifth Chakra, giving us a strong energy field and strengthening the power of our word to keep us on our path. Highly creative, this meditation boosts our discipline and infuses us with self-confidence.

Sit in Easy Pose with a straight spine and apply a slight Neck Lock (tucking the chin slightly back toward the spine). Focus your eyes at the tip of your nose. Bring your palms facing your body and interlace your fingers (thumbs stay up). Bend the middle and ring fingers back so they are pressing against each other with moderate force. Keep the rest of your fingers straight. This mudra represents discipline and the energy of life. Keep your arms parallel to the ground and at a straight line, keeping the mudra in front of your throat.

Inhale deeply and chant the mantra, **Ong Kar,** five times on one breath. Inhale and continue chanting in this manner for up to **31 minutes.** This mantra unifies us with all of creation, and is a kind of ego-antidote.

For the first **5 minutes**, keep a steady pressure of about 10-15 pounds on your fingers. For the final **5 minutes,** pull harder, with a pressure of about 25-50 pounds. (If you pull very hard, with a 50-pound pressure, limit your practice to **11 minutes**.)

While chanting, feel the central channel of the spine. Feel the flow of energy up your spine. With each inhale feel the breath go all the way to the navel. Stay present and allow the force of the mantra to change the energy of your thoughts from the inside out. This will transform you.

To End: Inhale deeply, suspend the breath, and turn your eyes to the Brow Point, the point between your eyebrows. Exhale and repeat two more times. Inhale and stretch the hands up. Move and shake, especially your fingers and hands, stretch all of your muscles and relax.

For Total Mental Balance

Sometimes you just need to listen to the voice of your own soul. You need to carve out some time to be gentle with your body and kind to your spirit. You need to clear the fog of despair from your mind and enter into a place beyond time and space where there is only peace. Kirtan Kriya is a bridge from where you are to what you want to feel. It is said to assist you in knowing the unknown and seeing the unseen. Scientific research has found that it helps restore memory loss and prevent the shortening of telomeres, which is a key factor in aging. When you feel like your mind is out of balance and you can't right yourself, try Kirtan Kriya.

Meditation: Kirtan Kriya

This meditation is one of the three meditations that Yogi Bhajan, the master of Kundalini Yoga, said would carry humanity forward if all the other teachings of Kundalini Yoga were lost. It's an extraordinary practice. This meditation brings total mental balance and awakens the mind to the Infinite capacity of the soul.

Sit in Easy Pose with a straight spine and a slight Neck Lock. Shut your eyes and focus them in and up toward the Brow Point.

 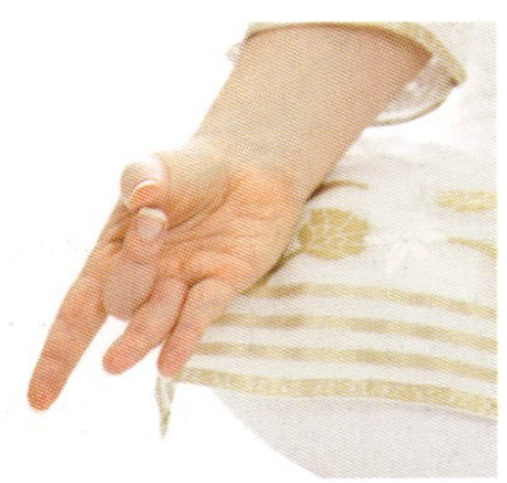  

Keep your elbows straight and rest the back of your hands on your knees. Beginning with your hands in Gyan Mudra, one at a time you will touch your thumb to your forefinger, middle finger, ring finger, and pinkie with a firm but gentle pressure. As you press the fingers together, you will chant the mantra **Sa Ta Na Ma**, which means Inifinity, Life, Death, Rebirth, and invokes a transformation and rebirth of consciousness.

SA — Press the Jupiter (index) finger and thumb
TA — Press the Saturn (middle) finger and thumb
NA — Press the Sun (ring) finger and thumb
MA — Press the Mercury (pinkie) finger and thumb

Each repetition of the mantra should take 3-4 seconds. The mantra is chanted in the three languages of consciousness:

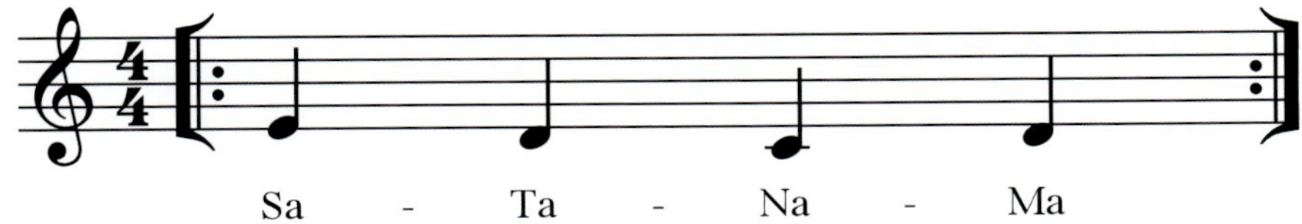

Aloud (the voice of the human) — awareness of the things of the world
Whisper (the voice of the lover) — experiencing the longing to belong
Silent (the voice of the divine) — vibration of Infinity

Follow this pattern of voices:

Chant aloud for **5 minutes**.
Then whisper for **5 minutes**.
Then go deeply into silence, mentally vibrating the sound for **10 minutes**.
Then whisper for **5 minutes**.
Then chant aloud for **5 minutes**.

While chanting, visualize the flow of the sounds in an "L" form. As you meditate feel there is a constant inflow of cosmic energy into your Crown Chakra. As the energy enters the top of the head, move the sounds *Sa, Ta, Na, Ma* through the Crown Chakra and project it out through the Third Eye. As you chant **Sa**, for example, the "S" starts at the top of the head and the "A" moves down and out through the Brow Point. This follows the pathway called the Golden Cord, the connection between the pineal and pituitary glands. Some people may occasionally experience headaches because of improper circulation of prana if they do not use this "L" form. Wrapping the head in a cloth or turban can help prevent this, and with time and focus on the "L" shape, headaches will lessen.

To End: Deeply inhale and suspend the breath as long as comfortable, up to **1 minute**. Sit in absolute stillness and silence. Then stretch your hands up as far as possible and spread your fingers wide. Stretch your spine and take several nourishing breaths. Relax.

Comforting Your Soul

Chanting is a comforting practice. It allows you to wrap yourself in a cocoon of high vibration and turn your mind onto a practice that protects you from self-harm and self-loathing. If your mind is filled with mantra, it is very difficult to fill your mind with critical thoughts. The mantra used in this meditation is like a boat across a stormy sea. It invites protection and comfort. Sing yourself back into health and happiness.

Meditation: Weaving Mudra Meditation

Originally taught by Yogi Bhajan: July 29, 1986

This meditation is for balance when you are in pain, have slow circulation, or are stuck in phobias. It works on both the Navel Center and the brain.

Sit in Easy Pose with a straight spine. Make scissors of your Jupiter (index) and Saturn (middle) fingers and then interlock them so that the Saturn finger of your right hand is on the back of your left hand. Curl your pinky and ring fingers back into the palm and lift your thumbs up until they touch each other and form a point. This is Weaving Mudra; place the mudra against your diaphragm. Pull your navel in and chant Rakhay Rakanhaar* for **22 minutes**.

Ramdesh's Insight: Because this meditation works on phobias and slow circulation, it is particularly suited to anorexics.

Rakhay rakhanhaar aap ubaarian
Gur kee pairee paa-eh kaaj savaarian
Hoaa aap dayaal manho na visaarian
Saadh janaa kai sang bhavajal taarian
Saakat nindak dusht khin maa-eh bidaarian
Tis saahib kee tayk naanak manai maa-eh
Jis simarat sukh ho-eh sagalay dookh jaa-eh

* For more about this mantra, see page 102.

Relaxing the Grip of Negativity

In Kundalini Yoga philosophy, it is said that there are three minds: Positive, Negative, and Neutral. The Positive Mind sees the opportunity in everything; it helps us find a way forward and create what we want. The Negative Mind protects us from harm, finds potential pitfalls, and warns us of danger. The Neutral Mind sits like a judge between the two, evaluating the case for positive and negative, and striving to make balanced and intuitive decisions. If the Positive Mind is weak and the Negative Mind too strong, all the judge can hear is the case against. Recovery from an eating disorder, where we have caused our bodies and minds so much harm, requires that we relax the grip of the Negative Mind. In being overly self-critical, we reinforce the muscle of our Negative Mind and it gets out of balance. If we allow this state to persist, false memories, slanted toward the Negative Mind, can hypnotize and distract us. Traumas can affect us even more intensely, disrupting our True Identity. If we allow the imprint of an overactive Negative Mind to stay with us for too long, we can become depressed and detached.

Meditation: For the Negative Mind

This meditation helps us to balance the Negative Mind, so we can learn to be wise, avoid past temptations, and let go of what doesn't serve us in the here and now. This breathing exercise helps you drop the past, find your real self, and move forward into a brighter life.

Sit in Easy Pose with a straight spine. Focus your eyes at the tip of your nose.

Touch the fingertips of your hands together forming a tent shape and hold your hands in front of your solar plexus. Make sure your fingertips are spread and facing forward.

Inhale deeply through your nose and suspend your breath chanting **Sa Ta Na Ma** once. Then exhale in eight equal strokes through a rounded mouth. The exhale should not come from the tip of the lips, but rather from the middle of the mouth. The breath is generated from the Navel Center. By the final exhale, pull your navel back toward your spine as far as you can. Continue for **11 minutes**. You can work your way up to **31 minutes**.

Connecting with Your True Self

Sometimes the most powerful part of healing is to recognize that you are not this body or this mind or this challenge you are going through. These are experiences you are having; as long as you are relating to your finite self, the part of you that is walking on this earth, it's difficult to unstick yourself from identifying with yourself as a body. Then you place judgments on this body like "I'm too fat" or "I'm ugly." Perhaps you flip that script and you obsess about how beautiful you are and become convinced you are better than others. When you identify with your Infinite Self instead of your finite self, you take yourself out of this conversation completely. As you realize your physical body is impermanent, you won't feel the same need to be physically perfect. Your body is a precious vessel for you to take care of, keep healthy, and honor, but it's not who you truly are.

With this realization, you begin to treat yourself compassionately and kindly, adorning your Body Temple rather than masking yourself, nourishing yourself rather than punishing yourself with food. At the very least, this meditation below can connect you with a true sense of who you are and give you the chance to breathe and free your spirit from the weight of your mental stresses. This powerful meditation to take your into the core of your Infinite Self is a kind, and loving meditation, and no matter who you are, we can all stand to treat ourselves kindly and lovingly.

Meditation: Into Being

Originally taught by Yogi Bhajan: April 1972

The mantra, *I am, I Am,* connects your finite identity with your Infinite self. The first "I am" refers to your finite self and the second "I *Am*" refers to your impersonal self. This mantra meditation expands your sense of self-awareness and embodies personal authenticity and wholeness in every part of your experience.

Sit in Easy Pose with a slight Neck Lock. Keep your eyes 9/10th shut and look straight ahead through your eyelids. Your right hand is in Gyan Mudra (thumb and forefinger touching) resting on your right knee. Your left hand is raised in front of the Heart Center, palm facing in.

Start with your left hand 6 inches out from your chest; as you move toward the chest (about 2 inches), chant "**I am**."

Then chant "**I Am**" again as you draw your left hand away from the chest (about 12 inches). Take a small, short breath through the nose as you draw the hand back to the original position and continue.

Create a steady rhythm back and forth **I am, I Am** toward and away from your chest. Continue for **11-31 minutes**.

To End: Inhale deeply, hold your breath and relax.

Easing Day-to-Day Problems

Recovering from an eating disorder or a lifetime of self-neglect requires taking it one day at a time. You have to slowly unpeel the layers of negativity that you or other people have put into you, unwind your mind's habits of negative thinking, smooth out some of the challenges of day-to-day life, and begin to direct your projection toward a positive future. Having a boost of luck and prosperity can help you believe that lasting healing is possible and that maybe, just maybe, life is better without an eating disorder and that life is better when you love yourself. Because it is. I'm living proof. I promise that every single breath of your life feels better when you fill yourself with love.

Meditation: Ganpati Kriya

Originally taught by Yogi Bhajan: January 1988

This meditation is said to release the impact of past and present negativity; it will change your luck and allow prosperity to flow.

Mantra: **Sa Ta Na Ma Ra Ma Da Sa Sa Say So Hung**

Chant the mantra on a single breath, as you press the fingertips of each hand sequentially (thumb to forefinger, thumb to middle finger, thumb to ring finger, thumb to pinky finger) with each syllable. Use a monotone voice. Continue for **11 minutes**.

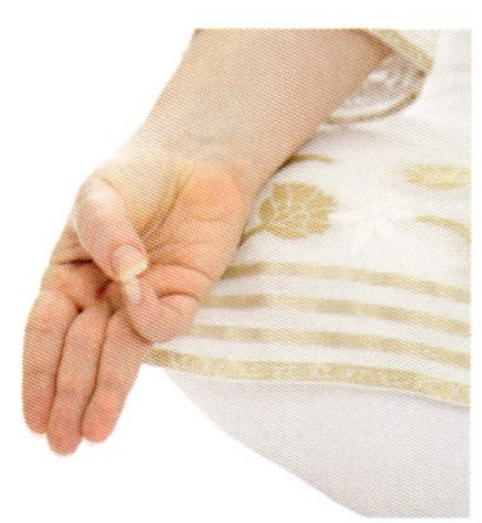

To End: Inhale deeply and hold your breath. Move your body in a slow twisting and stretching motion. Move each muscle of your body. Move your head, torso, arms, back, belly, and hands. Then exhale powerfully. Repeat this 5 times.

Using Breath to Heal

For many of us, especially those who are overweight or underweight, our challenges can't be hidden, which increases the intense feelings of shame. Let's say you injured your back and can't exercise, or you've had a child and the baby weight hasn't come off, or you've worked at a desk for a few years, and now you've gained 60 pounds. You don't relate to being as heavy as you are and feel uncomfortable in your new body. You don't feel sexy, you don't feel vital, and you start to hide behind baggy, unflattering clothing. Self-esteem plummets and you feel like you have failed. It's a common story for people who experience weight gain. But you haven't done anything wrong; your soul could never do anything wrong, you are simply living an experience. If you are ready for a new experience, ready to release feelings of guilt and shame, try this simple breathing technique.

Meditation: Healing Pranayam–Self-Care Breath

Originally taught by Yogi Bhajan: May 8, 1995

This breathing exercise increases your energy, boosts your immune system, cleanses your body, releases guilt, and restores self-esteem.

Sit in Easy Pose and cross your hands over your heart, right over left. Make a very precise and tight "O" shape with your mouth. Close your eyes and focus on your Heart Center. Breathe in a steady, powerful Cannon Breath through the mouth, inhaling powerfully and forcefully exhaling, with a booming sound. Imagine that you are shaping your breath into an "O" ring from the shape of your mouth. Continue for **5 minutes**.

To End: Inhale and hold your breath. Relax your mouth and mentally repeat "**I am beautiful. I am innocent. I am innocent. I am beautiful.**" Exhale through your nose. Repeat this 5 times. Relax.

Eliminating Thoughts You Dislike

If your inner narrative is negative, don't skip over this meditation. If you tell yourself that you are fat and ugly, or that you're not thin enough or beautiful enough to do yoga in a class setting—where you think everyone will look like a model—or if somehow every time you take three steps forward to self-love, you take three steps back as the voice in your head starts spinning out cruel, mean words that hurt you deeply and you find all too easy to believe, do this meditation to strengthen your positive self-talk and eliminate the thoughts you dislike.

The three minds (Positive, Negative, and Neutral) each have important functions. When the Positive Mind is weak, its ability to project possibilities is limited. The ego, seizing its moment, preempts the Positive Mind's expansive nature and spins a narrative that is harsh and controlling, keeping you small and under its control. Whatever words impact you the most teach the ego where to push you more. So if the word "fat" is a trigger for you, the ego will exploit the weakness of your Positive Mind and push this trigger word into your inner narrative repeatedly. This meditation helps you change that inner narrative to a positive one and begin to make faster, more unimpeded steps towards radiant inner joy. It can be especially helpful for someone who is trying to shift a pattern like purging, because it gives you a way to expel energy and push discomfort out of the body, while maintaining a peaceful center.

Meditation: Eliminating Thoughts You Dislike

When you have a persistent negative thought, practice this meditation to release it so that your Positive Mind can become stronger and positive thoughts can manifest without obstruction. The life you create for yourself is a reflection of what is going on in your inner world; if you can stop negative thinking in its tracks, and move past the habituated thinking that is not loving and not supportive, your outer world will shift into a more graceful, easy alignment of positivity.

Sit in Easy Pose with a straight spine. Cup your hands in front of your Heart Center, right hand over the left. Gaze into your palms.

Ramdesh's Insight: This is a great meditation to try if you only have a few minutes or if you think you can't meditate. Start with a 3-minute practice and see how quickly your thoughts can shift!

Meditate deeply on the thoughts you would like to eliminate. Inhale through your nose and then exhale through puckered lips, blowing out the negative thought you are focusing on into your palms in a long, slow breath. Keep your mind focused on and thinking about all the mean, limiting, negative thoughts you think regularly. Continue for up to **11 minutes**.

Ramdesh's Insight: Although not part of the meditation, I love to follow this practice with positive thoughts. I play uplifting, beautiful music that affirms self-love and happiness, immediately giving my Positive Mind reinforcement and nurturing. Plus, it just feels good to sing along to something inspiring.

To End: Inhale deeply and exhale. Close your eyes and focus on every vertebra in your spine from top to bottom. The harder you focus on your spine, the more healing will occur as energy flows through your entire body, replacing negativity with positive energy.

Healing from Family Trauma

For many people with eating disorders, low self-esteem, or negative self-image, the root cause of these patterns began in early childhood. According to the National Eating Disorders Association, it is estimated that 30% of people with eating disorders are survivors of trauma including physical, verbal, or sexual abuse. These early childhood traumas create phobias within us. Perhaps we develop a phobia around men when a father or uncle abuses us, and become fearful of deeply resonant, loving connections with men. Many personality imbalances are caused by early trauma. Traumas don't have to be physically violent. Infants and young children are so sensitive that an argument with our parents when we're a newborn, for example, can impact our psyches in ways we don't realize. Perhaps as a child you were told you were ugly or you were punished if you weren't perfect. There are a million scenarios that your subconscious can still be replaying. To remove them once and for all, a powerful meditation is needed. Tershula Kriya, often called the Thunderbolt of Shiva, is a powerful meditation to transform your personality from the inside out and from the past to the present.

Meditation: Tershula Kriya

Tershula is the thunderbolt of Shiva the Destroyer. It is a powerful self-healing practice that stimulates the Kundalini energy, it can heal many psychological disorders and personality imbalances, and gives you powerful healing abilities to share with others. It is particularly effective in getting rid of phobias, including father phobia. This meditation is recommended to be practiced at night or in a cool place, as it generates a great deal of heat within the body.

Sit in Easy Pose with a slightly tucked chin. Close your eyes and visualize yourself looking at the back of your eyelids. Bring your elbows to your ribs and extend your hands out in front of you. Place the right hand over the left, palms up, with the middle finger of the right hand aligned with the tip of the forefinger of the left hand; and the forefinger of the right hand aligned with the middle finger of the left. The thumbs are extended out to the sides and the hands are 10 degrees higher than your elbows. Keep your wrists straight so that your arms form a straight line from elbow to fingertip. Hold this posture throughout the meditation.

To Practice: Inhale through your nose, pull in your navel and suspend your breath. As you hold your breath in, mentally chant the mantra **Har Har Waheguru** (which translates as Creator! Creator! Ecstasy here and now, from Darkness to Light!) as long as you are able. While mentally chanting, imagine that you are surrounded by bright white light. Exhale through your nose and visualize lightening shooting out from your fingertips. When you have completely exhaled, hold your breath out, pull Root Lock (Mulbandh) and mentally chant the mantra as long as you can. Release the Root Lock (relaxing your muscles) and inhale deeply.

Continue in this pattern for **31-62 minutes**.

Creating the Future You Want

There is a process that I used as a part of my psychotherapy called scripting. It's where you write exactly what you want your life to look like. I suggest it as a supplementary process to encourage you to engage in becoming the conscious author of your own life. It's an empowering way of moving yourself forward. If you don't know what you want, you're not likely to get it, and you're significantly less likely to arrive in a place you're happy about.

This meditation isn't quite scripting, but it works on the same principle. It focuses the mind's projective capacity onto a specific word target and allows your energy field to come into conscious alignment with the frequency of that word. In essence it allows you to send a single code into the program of your future and to lock onto the one thing that you want more than anything.

For some of you, the word that will come up is "thin." Most often for people with eating disorders it's the one thing they want so much they're willing to die for it. So if you have an eating disorder, I'd like to ask you *not* to use the word thin, but instead to consciously embrace your healing and project into the future a world that has nothing to do with your weight and your body image. Create the future you would want if you already loved your body. What would you think about then? Think about how much mental and emotional energy you would instantly free up to create and produce and dream and play. The purpose of your life is joy. Don't forget it.

Meditation: Beaming and Creating the Future

Originally taught by Yogi Bhajan: June 12, 1990

This meditation is recommended on an empty stomach, so practice it first thing in the morning to help you set the intention for your entire day. You might choose to do this meditation after a kriya, as it will help you release distracting thoughts from your mind and focus with laser-like intensity on what you want to create.

Part One

Sit in Easy Pose with a straight spine and become very still. Close your eyes and relax your hands into Gyan Mudra (thumb and forefinger touching) on your knees. Begin breathing by drinking in air through your mouth as if sipping through a straw. Drink long and deep through your "O"-shaped mouth and exhale slowly and completely through your nose. **7-15 minutes**.

Part Two

Inhale and hold your breath. Meditate on zero by thinking, *"All is zero. I am zero. Each thought is zero. My pain is zero. That problem is zero. That illness is zero."* Take it all into nothingness. Meditate on all negative, emotional, mental, and physical conditions and situations. As you think of each thing, mentally bring it to zero. If you have an eating disorder, shrink it to zero. Shrink each condition down to a tiny point of light and let it pass into nothing. Exhale and repeat. Breath in a comfortable rhythm. **7-11 minutes**.

Part Three

Think of the quality or condition you most desire for happiness.

Summarize what would bring you happiness into a single word such as "health," "success," "wealth," "relationship," "wisdom," or whatever word comes into your mind. Choose a single word to lock onto. Once you have locked onto a word, visualize it, look at all sides of it. Inhale, suspend your breath and beam that word out into the creative consciousness of the Universe. Imagine that you are continuously emitting a stream of energy that vibrates the energy of that word. Focus with the clarity of a laser on beaming that word into the future. Relax your breath as necessary and continue for **5-15 minutes**.

To End: Raise your arms and hands up, lengthen your spine, and spread your fingers wide. Breathe deeply. Inhale and exhale a few times, stretching your arms and spine.

Ramdesh's Insight*:* I would encourage you not to think of something that is body-conscious here, although Yogi Bhajan did not teach this meditation with limits. For purposes of recovery, try not to focus on being thin or some definition of beauty. Choose another attribute.

Blossoming into Your Potential

By not allowing our love for ourselves to bloom, our destiny never blossoms either. A lack of self-love holds us back and keeps us small. We are all destined for so much more than we allow ourselves to live. Sit silently and breathe deeply. Ask yourself what your full potential is. Visualize a small pinprick of light. Now imagine this light explodes. Imagine that it expands into a whole ocean of light. You are that ocean, but you try to contain yourself in the pinprick. Of course your body feels uncomfortable! You must let your soul out to feel the fullness of its experience, to feel free and Infinite, so that your body does not become a cage, but rather a vessel.

When you begin to feel overwhelmed, as if you are praying and affirming and trying to manifest health, healing, and love, but it doesn't seem to be coming your way, try this meditation. It helps bring your head and your heart together so that the longing of your soul is heard and felt.

Meditation: To Blossom into Your Full Potential

Originally taught by Yogi Bhajan: January 29, 1979

When you feel like your prayers and intentions aren't working, this meditation helps shift resistance so they start to flow, allowing you to blossom into your full potential. This meditation activates the vagus nerve, increasing calm and supporting clear communication between your heart and your brain.

Sit in Easy Pose with a straight spine. Rest your right hand in your left hand, palms facing up, and position your hands about 1 inch above the Navel Center. Press your thumb tips together. Inhale and chant the mantra in a monotone. Keep your pronunciation and rhythm precise. Each word gets one beat. Continue for up to **31 minutes.**

Sat Nam Sat Nam Sat Nam Sat Nam
Sat Nam Sat Nam Sat Nam Wah Guru

Ramdesh's Insight: This mantra uses **Wah Guru**, not *Waheguru*. **He** is a grounding vibration that pulls the energy of the mantra down into the body. By using the form **Wah** instead of *Wahe*, the resonance is up and out, connecting to Infinity, which allows the spirit to unfold outwards and expansively, and blossom into Infinity.

Learning to Accept Yourself

When we become divided from our true nature, self-animosity, self-hate, and self-defeating behaviors arise. When we don't accept ourselves deeply and infuse our lives with conscious self-love and self-care, we self-sabotage and our spirits feel caged. If we don't have a strong creative outlet that feeds our soul, and if we don't honor ourselves and our path, our mind rebels and turns on itself.

Self-animosity begins with something feeling wrong. Often we don't know what exactly is wrong with us, but we feel that there is something deeply wrong at our core: that we aren't enough, whatever enough means. Our understanding of our own vital worth becomes disrupted, and we begin to resent ourselves for being too fat, too stupid, too ugly, too lazy, too much or too little—too whatever—it's all a distortion of reality and it's never true. To heal from self-hate, we have to come to deeply accept ourselves, trusting that we are enough, just as we are, in every moment.

Meditation: To Conquer Self-Animosity

Originally taught by Yogi Bhajan: March 1979

This meditation disrupts the cycle of self-animosity and teaches us to live in service and support of our higher consciousness.

Sit in Easy Pose with a light Neck Lock. Stay alert. Relax your elbows at your sides and raise your hands in front of the chest; make fists of your hands, and point your thumbs straight up. Your thumbs and fists are touching. Keep your torso straight and motionless, and fix your eyes at the tip of your nose.

Inhale through your nose and exhale through your mouth. Inhale deeply through your mouth and exhale through your nose. Continue alternating your inhale/exhale pattern. Continue for **3 minutes**. Gradually work up to **11 minutes**. This practice should not exceed **22 minutes**.

To End: Inhale and stretch your arms up over your head. Keep your arms up as you take three more deep breaths. Relax.

The Last Resort

A time may come when you feel like you are at your wit's end. You feel a great need for help. You may even feel that you cannot survive one more day. Find the strength to do this meditation on that day. This is your last resort, and it gives you the strength to lift yourself out of sadness and find the best of yourself again. You deserve it.

Meditation: The Last Resort Meditation

Originally taught by Yogi Bhajan: June 15, 1982

Sit in Easy Pose with a straight spine. Rest your hands in your lap, palms facing up, right hand resting in the left. Touch your thumb tips together. Close your eyes and chant in a monotone, 8 times on one breath.

Waheguru Waheguru Waheguru Wahejio

You will need to take a very big breath in order to fill your lungs enough to chant the complete mantra. If you can't make it 8 rounds, stop, inhale again, and build up your capacity. Release your breath slowly as you chant to be able to carry the full mantra. Start with **11 minutes**, build to **22 minutes** and then to **31 minutes**.

When he taught this meditation, Yogi Bhajan said,

"This meditation brings relaxation, strength, and mental clarity. It brings soul talk—the infinite capacity to experience the power of your soul right on the spot. . . . If you do this meditation for 11 minutes a day for six months, you will experience the cosmos. You can talk to God. If you do it for a year, God will come and listen to you! Remember: you breathe, you live, because there is a soul in you. The soul is a tiny tender light in your body. I'm giving you a meditation today. I call it the "Last Meditation." It is not that it is the last meditation I will teach you. But understand its essence. It is for when life doesn't work for you, and you don't want to go to anybody and say, 'I'm going crazy, please help me.' I understand that sometimes personal image is very important. Despite how depressed you may be, just do this meditation and find out for yourself.

Kundalini Yoga is a science and an art which can totally make a human being healthy, happy, and holy. The mantra means: You are beloved of my Soul, Oh God. The practice of this will enable you to think right, act right, see right, look at yourself, imagine and meditate. Everything else follows. You will wipe out a lot of negativity. Many things will happen in my absence which you need to survive . . . . if you can do this meditation correctly, you will come out with the best of yourself. Please participate with heart and mind, and see that you do it."

I make healthy choices.

CHAPTER 10

Loving Relationship with Food

"You are not eating food, you are eating for your health, your vitality, your energy, your prosperity, your strength. . . "

~ Yogi Bhajan, August 13, 1992

TRANSFORMING YOUR RELATIONSHIP WITH FOOD

A perfect body isn't a magazine pin-up; a perfect body is one that is cared for and honored. Your Body Temple needs high-quality nourishment. It needs love and care and mineral support. Food is not the problem. Food is a life-giving tool for providing our bodies with the care they need. The problem is the stress we have about food and the unhealthy ways we use it. The perfect body, the true Body Temple, is one that is allowed to feel joy, and that includes joy in food.

Herbs that support eating disorder recovery:

Acidophilus:
intestinal flora

Astragalus:
adrenal glands

Brewer's Yeast:
nervous system

Licorice Root:
digestive health

Nutmeg:
brain health

Ginseng:
general tonic

Zinc:
immune system

St. John's Wort:
mental health

This chapter is not about diet. A wise friend of mine once told me to eliminate the word diet from my vocabulary. She said that the word diet itself includes the word die, which triggers your subconscious to believe that you are in mortal danger. A diet will never feel supportive or nourishing to our subconscious. For many of us with a history of eating disorders, diets are also triggers that can impede healing. Instead of using food to manage your stress or restricting it to manage your weight, shift your mindset around food and use it to nourish your body. Choose nutritionally dense, life-sustaining foods. Wholesome, fresh, and natural food is healing and enlivening to your precious Body Temple. Embrace the foods the Earth provides as a part of your divine inheritance: vegetables, fruits, nuts, and seeds. Consider essential vitamins, minerals, and amino acids to support your body. Imagine they are food for the soul as well as your soul's vehicle, your body, because a healthy body supports the flourishing of your spirit!

FOOD AS THE ULTIMATE PRANA

Prana is life-force vitality, and food inherently has its own prana, just as our bodies do. Chemical-laden, highly processed foods have very little prana and are deadening to the energy in our bodies. Other foods that drain our pranic reserves and should be avoided are sugar, caffeine, white flour, and alcohol. For maximum vitality, eat foods that are grown with lots of sunshine, clean water, and rich soil. Start to feel the prana in your foods as a part of how you select food to purchase. Make friends with the farmers at your local farmers' market. Allow what you eat to be a healing balm for your body and spirit, and a constant replenishing source of powerful prana. Don't beat yourself up, however, if your food choices aren't perfect; instead put self-love in all things, including what you eat.

PRANAYAM TO HELP YOUR FOOD ADDICTION

Many people have a strong addiction to food. The addiction meditation in this book can work well with any type of addiction—food, drug, or alcohol. When recovering from an addiction, it can be useful to use the acronym HALT, Hungry Angry Lonely Tired, which reminds you to be aware of what can trigger you. Although it is not a part of the tradition of Kundalini Yoga, it is common in the world of recovery. I consider stress a part of Tired and boredom a part of Lonely, if those words resonate more deeply with you.

"Eat what you want to eat, but don't let yourself be eaten up by the food."

~ Yogi Bhajan

There is a practice called Sitali Pranayam that addresses these core emotional triggers. It pacifies anxiety, anger, agitation, and heat within your system. When you feel HALT, before heading into the kitchen or to your secret stash of food, try using this breathing exercise to shift your mind's focus to one of peace and calm.

Sitali Pranayam

Sit in Easy Pose with a straight spine. Curl the tongue and extend the tip of the tongue just past your lips. (It helps to slightly pucker the lips.) Inhale deeply through the rolled tongue. Exhale completely through the nose. Continue for a minimum of 1-3 minutes and gradually increase to **31 minutes**.

PRANAYAM TO HELP WITH FOOD TRIGGERS

Whether you overeat or undereat, keep your Body Temple tools handy, and if you find yourself becoming triggered, turn to a mantra or a pranayam. When I find myself triggered at the refrigerator, or indulging in a trigger food that makes me want to binge, I often use this simple pranayama to get my mind straight. It has helped me stop the urge to binge and purge in its tracks. Originally a breathing exercise taught for stress relief by Yogi Bhajan, I find it very helpful to relieve the mind from compulsion in the moment—and it works quickly, which is critical in the middle of a compulsive thought or feeling. Stress is a huge trigger for many with eating disorders or anxiety around food. A stressful day can send you reaching for a gallon of ice cream as a default. So put a little note on your refrigerator that says, "Remember to Breathe," or "8-Part Breath," and let it remind you when you compulsively reach for food on a stressful day to try this instead (in a pinch, you can even do this while you are standing in the kitchen with a fork or spoon in your hand about to start overeating and stop your behaviors in their tracks).

8-Stroke Breathing for Stress Relief

Sit in any comfortable meditative posture with a straight spine. Close your eyes and inhale through your nose in eight equal strokes. Exhale through your nose in one deep, powerful stroke. Continue for up to **11 Minutes**. (Give **3 Minutes** a try to start.)

To End: Inhale deeply, hold your breath for 5-10 seconds, and exhale. Inhale deeply, hold your breath for 15-20 seconds and roll your shoulders. Exhale powerfully. Inhale deeply, hold your breath again for 15-20 seconds, and this time roll your shoulders as fast as you can. Exhale and relax.

MAKE YOUR DINING EXPERIENCE SACRED

Give Bhoj Kriya a try for learning conscious eating... You'll find it in the Kriya section of the book.

Try meditating before you eat so you can arrive at the table with a clear mind. Hold your hands over your food and send pranic energy into the food, blessing the soil that grew it, the people who harvested it and cooked it, and you who are eating it. In the Kundalini Yoga community, it is traditional to bless the food by putting your hands in prayer pose at your Heart Center and chanting a long Sat Nam three times to raise the vibration of the food and bring your body into perfect alignment. Bless yourself and your body with the nourishment of a healthy, energetically uplifting meal. Blessing your food also helps to bring you into conscious awareness and turn your attention to what you are eating. Bring mindfulness into the entire experience, eating consciously bite by bite. By eating in full awareness, it is much easier to listen to your body and know when you are full and prevent overeating.

Before eating, you might say a blessing such as, "*Infinite Divine, allow this food to nourish and bless my body. Let it bring energy and light into my Body Temple, that I might feel beautiful, healthy, and whole. Help me to listen to the signals from my body, so that I know when I am still hungry and when I have had enough to eat. Sat Nam.*

With patience and grace, you can turn mealtime from a *scared* act into a *sacred* act, one day at a time.

STRONGER AURAS MAKE FOR HEALTHIER CHOICES

The stronger your aura, the easier it will be to automatically make healthy food choices. Your aura feels all the emotions in your field, so when you experience an uncomfortable emotion like depression or anxiety, the aura shrinks and your energy field becomes weak. Many people with a weak aura reach for food to boost their energy artificially, but it never lasts and is often accompanied by a crash, especially when sugar is the energy boost of choice. When our aura is strong, we experience fewer cravings for the foods we typically reach for when our aura is weak. Sugar and junk foods are common aura crutches, but they have addictive properties that further deplete our vitality. By boosting the aura with yoga, pranayam, meditation, good foods, and mantra, our cravings subside.

If you are really struggling with a food addiction, try this one simple change, which doesn't involve food at all! Take a cold shower in the morning. Cold water hydrotherapy, known as ishnaan, is a simple aura booster that isn't directly related to your addiction, so your ego is less likely to dig its heels in and make the change more difficult. Simply take a cold shower for a few minutes each morning, feel your aura get stronger, and see if that doesn't help you find the strength to change your relationship to food.

HEALTHY RECIPES FOR YOUR BODY TEMPLE

Yogi Bhajan passed down many Ayurvedic recipes for food as medicine. Here I have shared a few rejuvenating recipes from that tradition, as well as some loving, heart-filled recipes of my own that I use to nurture myself. My secret ingredient for all food is mantra. I usually have mantra playing aloud and often sing mantra into my food as I prepare it, for extra healing. Try some of these healing, nurturing recipes out for yourself, and remember to stir in your favorite mantra!

To begin with, all food was considered human medicine. Food is the medicine which creates equilibrium.

~ Yogi Bhajan, *Beads of Truth*, Winter 1992

Yogi Bhajan's Yogi Tea Recipe

Yogi Tea is a staple for every Kundalini Yoga home and yoga center. It is an excellent nervous system tonic, gives mental balance, boosts the immune system, purifies the blood, and gives an energy boost. It's an excellent substitute for coffee, which can be very harsh to the nervous system.

10 oz. water
3 cloves
4 whole green cardamom pods
4 whole black peppercorns
2 slices of fresh ginger root
½ stick cinnamon
1 teabag of black tea or ¼ tsp. loose black tea (optional but highly recommended to bind everything together and help in assimilation)
(Added after) ½ cup milk & honey to taste

Combine all spices except black tea with water and boil 10-15 min. Longer is stronger. Remove from heat. Then, add black teabag and boil for another 1-2 minutes. Add milk. Milk helps cut the bite of the spices and make it gentler on your stomach. Add honey to taste. Strain and serve. If you plan to keep the tea in the fridge, do not add milk and honey until you pour and reheat your tea. It will keep fresh longer.

Yogi Bhajan's Golden Milk

Turmeric is a powerful root from India commonly used in Ayurvedic preparations. It cleanses the liver, promotes digestion, improves skin, and reduces joint pain.

Golden Milk is a wonderful traditional recipe to nourish yourself and your joints on a cold night. This recipe would work brilliantly for people who are underweight, undernourished, and feeling pain in their joints.

⅛ tsp. turmeric
¼ cup water
8 oz. milk
2 Tbsp. almond oil
Honey (to taste)

Boil water and turmeric in saucepan over medium-high heat for 8 minutes. Make sure the turmeric is fully cooked. Bring the milk and almond oil to a boil in a separate pan, then remove from heat. Combine the two mixtures and add honey to taste.

Ramdesh's Insight: Dairy is a common ingredient in Ayurvedic recipes. While you may substitute your preferred vegan milk such as almond milk or coconut milk, the chemistry of the original recipe is altered and may not have the same effect.

Yogi Bhajan's Carrot and Garlic Juice

This juice recipe supports people struggling with addictions and helps eliminate sadness, negativity, and frustration. With strong amounts of Vitamins A and C, it also boosts your immune system. This juice is good for your nervous and cardiovascular systems and has anti-cancer properties. The strong orange color supports your Second Chakra.

6-8 oz. of carrot juice
¼ oz. of garlic juice (max)

Mix together and sip slowly.

Spirit Voyage's Kitcheree Recipe

Kitcheree is a staple of the Ayurvedic diet. It cleanses the colon, forms a highly digestible perfect protein, and is wonderful to build the immune system and restore nutritional health. It is a very restorative food to eat when you are feeling under the weather.

This recipe was shared with me by Karan Khalsa of Spirit Voyage, whose delicious cooking has often warmed my belly and my heart on cold days.

10 cups of water
2 cups basmati rice
2 cups whole green mung beans (soaked in water for at least 6 hours, but up to 24 hours)
1 medium onion (diced)
4 cloves garlic (finely chopped – you can use as much as a full bulb if you are a garlic lover)
1 to 2 inches ginger (finely chopped)
3 Tbsp. ghee (if you don't have ghee, olive oil can be substituted, but use a bit less)
1 Tbsp. turmeric
1 Tbsp. cumin seeds
1 Tbsp. coriander powder
1 Tbsp. crushed red chili flakes

1 tsp. Black Pepper
½ cup Bragg Liquid Aminos
1 lb. spinach (you can use any green leafy vegetable)
Fresh cilantro as garnish

Makes 10 servings.

Directions:

- Use the largest pot in your house for this recipe (8 qt. is ideal, but 5 qt. can work). Turn the heat to medium, and add the cumin seeds. Stir them occasionally until they start to pop.
- Then add the ghee, turmeric, coriander, and black pepper and stir to create a sauce. Let the spices cook together in the ghee for about a minute.
- Add the onions, garlic, and ginger and stir. Let cook for about 3 to 5 minutes until you can smell the onions and garlic cooking.
- Add 8 cups of water and the soaked mung beans. (The mung beans should have doubled in size while soaking).
- Cover and bring to a boil. Once the water is boiling, tilt the lid slightly but keep covered. Turn the temperature down to medium-low and allow to cook for 2 to 3 hours, adding water if necessary to keep it slightly soupy.
- After an hour, add the spinach.

If you have a pressure cooker, you can cook the mung bean part of the recipe in the pressure cooker for 25 minutes.

In a separate pot, cook the rice. Combine the rice with 5 cups of water. Add the crushed red chili flakes. Bring to a rolling boil and let boil for 7 minutes. Then turn off heat and cover for 20 minutes. Do not remove lid as the steam will continue to cook the rice, making it light and fluffy.

Check the mung beans from time to time. Once they are soft, they are done. You then turn off the heat and mix the rice in with the beans. Add the ½ cup of Bragg Liquid Aminos and stir together.

Your kitcheree is ready to serve. Try eating with plain yogurt and fresh cilantro. Delicious! After you let the pot cool, you can put the entire pot in the refrigerator and heat up individual servings all week!

Chia Seed Superfood Pudding

Chia Seed Pudding is one of my favorite things to make (and delicious to eat). Chia seeds are loaded with age-defying antioxidants, protein, fiber, healthy omega-3s, and are known to help regulate blood sugar. Highly prized by Aztecs and Mayans as a food source, the word "chia" means strength in the original language. Chia Seed Pudding is a healthy way to give your body a nourishing treat. It's simple to make; it just takes chia seeds, milk (almond, coconut, or rice milk all work for a vegan treat), and a natural sweetener (try agave nectar, maple syrup, or honey).

Here's my favorite Chia Seed Pudding recipe:

⅓ cup chia seed
1 ¼ cups rice milk
1 Tbsp. cacao powder
½ Tbsp. honey (to taste)
Handful of fresh blueberries

Mix all ingredients in a bowl. Stir until powders dissolve. Fold in fruit after other ingredients are mixed to prevent bruising. Set in the fridge until mixture forms pudding-like consistency.

Rainbow Salad

Color therapy can be a fun and healthy way to play with your food and make it a more spiritual experience. By eating the rainbow you are balancing your chakras and bringing the resonant energy of all healing colors into your body. This recipe is simply a salad with vegetables and fruits that bring all the colors of the rainbow to you. This is an excellent way to practice prana-filled food choices!

Some colorful suggestions:

Reds (First Chakra) — Red Pepper, Tomato, Radish
Oranges (Second Chakra) — Orange Pepper, Carrot, Mandarin Orange, Yam
Yellows (Third Chakra) — Yellow Pepper, Squash, Yellow Tomato, Yellow Radish
Greens (Fourth Chakra) — Lettuce, Broccoli, Zucchini, Celery, Cucumber, Bell Pepper
Blues (Fifth Chakra) — Blueberries
Indigo (Sixth Chakra) — Purple Cabbage, Beet, Purple Potato
Violet (Seventh Chakra) — Pomegranate, Lavender or Edible Flowers
Whites (Eighth Chakra) — Heart of Palm, Daikon Radish

Banana Ginger Recovery Smoothie

For those who are recovering from anorexia, making peace with food may be the hardest part of the journey to wellness. Often, liquid calories are easier to ingest than solid calories. If you are struggling with eating solid foods, try this delicious smoothie to get essential vitamins, minerals, and yes, life-giving calories. Feeling full can be very uncomfortable for recovering anorexics in particular, and smoothies do allow you to consume your food a little at a time to minimize that sensation. Be your best friend. Stay the course to health and wellness; encourage yourself to do the very best you can where you are today.

Protein is essential when you are underweight and rebuilding your body's health reserves; indeed, it can be a helpful tool for people with binge-eating tendencies too, as upping your protein intake can help manage cravings. Greek yogurt has nearly 20 grams of protein per serving, about double that of regular plain yogurt, and helps to repopulate the stomach with probiotics to aid in digestion. Greek yogurt is also an excellent source of B_{12} for energy and calcium for bone health. Ginger soothes the nervous and digestive systems, which eating disorders strain. It has been used for everything from nausea to backaches to headaches to colds. Bananas are high in many vitamins essential for women in particular, including potassium and phosphorus, and help balance the nervous system. Bananas also contain an amino acid called tryptophan, which is important in the manufacture of the mood-enhancing hormone serotonin.

Smoothies are a great way to incorporate additional foods into your meal. You can experiment by adding flax seeds for healthy omega oils, additional fruits for more vitamin punch, green tea for antioxidants, and more. Be creative and find what works best for you!

1 banana
1 cup plain Greek yogurt
½ tsp. of fresh ginger, chopped
½ cup ice
Honey or agave nectar (optional)

Blend everything together. Add sweetener optionally to taste. Enjoy.

Everyday I learn to love myself and my body more.

CHAPTER 11

A Lifestyle Program for Radical Self-Love

"You surrender to a lot of stuff which is worth nothing before you. I wish you should surrender to radiance, I wish you should surrender to your intelligence and integrity, I wish you should surrender to your beautiful human grace."

~ Yogi Bhajan, July 25, 1983

If your body is a temple, then your life is a worship service.

If you've been reading and practicing some ideas from this book, by now you're ready for some miraculous changes in your life and your lifestyle. And they will come, if you do the work, but the work isn't just doing some yoga and meditations. The work will require that you use every moment of your life as an opportunity to create a sacred space within you.

If your body is a temple, then your life is a worship service. If you want to live in harmony with this earth and all its occupants, you must live in harmony with yourself. Get to sacred living!

The Radical Self-Love Program:

40 Ways to Transform Your Life, Learn to Love Yourself, and Heal Your Relationship with Your Body

Forty is a powerful number. In this book, I've already shared the power of doing a meditation or kriya every day for 40 consecutive days to break a negative habit that is holding you back from living your best life. The number 40 holds power beyond the teachings of Kundalini Yoga. Across spiritual traditions, it represents a spiritual rebirth and the amount of time it takes to create a significant change. There are also 40 kriyas and meditations (plus some extra tools and techniques) in this book, so you can do a different one every day for 40 days and make it through a complete 40-day Kundalini Yoga practice. Or you can choose one (or several . . . go ahead and mix and match!) to dive deeper into for 40 days. Whether you are healing from an eating disorder or a lifetime of poor self-esteem, to pack a powerful punch into your program and truly transform in a radical way, making your life all about self-love—in addition to your yoga and meditation practice—is a deeply joyful way to honor the Body Temple.

Here are some of the religious examples of the power of the number 40:

Christianity
Number of days Jesus was in the desert

Judaism
Number of years the Jews wandered in the desert

Sikhism
Number of sections in the morning prayer Japji

Buddhism
Number of subjects considered fruitful to meditate upon

Islam
Age of the Prophet when Archangel Gabriel appeared to him

Even if you are not ready to commit to a 40-day program of excellence, try incorporating any or all of these techniques into your everyday living to create a sacred life and a Body Temple!

THE RADICAL SELF-LOVE PROGRAM

1 Daily Sadhana

A sadhana is a daily spiritual practice. In doing sadhana, you reserve a portion of your day for your own self-care. Do one kriya or meditation (or one of each) for 40 days until you have tried all of the practices in this book. How to choose? You can't get it wrong. Either choose one that feels like it speaks directly to what you are working on, go in order, or simply open the book randomly and trust that you are being guided to the right practice at the right time. Commit to a daily practice of yoga and meditation, even if only for 11 minutes. Choose longer "yoga days" when you have free time to explore more of the practices within this book for a few hours of yoga and chanting, but make sure that your main practice is consistent for 40 straight days.

2 Conscious Breath: Inhale Sat and Exhale Nam on Every Breath

For 40 days, commit to this simple technique that deepens your awareness of your breath, brings relaxation, and reduces stress; it also tricks your mind into replacing negative self-talk with a positive statement of your own truth. Inhale and mentally chant *Sat,* exhale and mentally chant *Nam*. Let it become the natural default setting in your mind, so that without even thinking about it, you find yourself

"To live positive and be positive requires a very powerful spiritual power, which is called love. . . . Love is a constant flow of that infinite power. Love represents God. Love represents you."

~ Yogi Bhajan
November 23, 1977

chanting in your mind, *Sat Nam, Sat Nam, Sat Nam*. Identifying with your Sat Nam, your True Identity, over any illusion of the physical form, is a crucial step in radical self-love.

3 Care for Yourself as a God/Goddess

Use body care routines like showering, bathing, brushing your teeth and hair to worship the goddess—or god—within. Make sure that you are using natural, organic skin and body care products so that you don't absorb toxins through your skin. Try using organic almond oil as an all-purpose body care product. As you take care of your body, talk to it: tell it that you love it, that you are grateful to it. If you can't think of anything nice to say, repeat "Bountiful am I. Beautiful am I. Blissful am I," over and over as you care for yourself.

4 Give Yourself a Foot Massage

Give yourself a foot massage, sending love to every organ and body system. Reflexology shows us that each major system and organ of the body has meridian points in the feet and that by massaging our feet, we can give healing energy to our entire body. Use almond oil, coconut oil, or mahanarayan oil for an extra boost of love. This is a perfect late night treat to help you fall quickly to sleep.

5 Delight Your Palette

Prepare prana-filled, nourishing food, and infuse it with sacred energy. Commit to 40 days of clean, loving eating. Try creating a mandala with colorful fruit to make it appealing and beautiful. Work with some of the recipes in this book or create your own, and strive to make meal time an act of self-love and self-care.

6 Keep a Sacred Space

Take care to keep your living environment clean and beautiful. Tidy up, vacuum, get rid of things you no longer need or want. Burn sage or Palo Santo to clear the energy of your space regularly. Or try Yogi Bhajan's recommendation: Use rose water and sandalwood along with sacred mantras to clear the energy of a room[35]. Light candles or salt lamps to create a sacred temple, and place sacred, energy-filled objects like crystals or flowers around your space. Consider the environment where you live a temple.

7 Morning Pep Talk

Spend 3 minutes first thing in the morning looking at yourself in the mirror and telling yourself that you love yourself. Set a timer. Consider it like brushing your teeth. You wake up, you brush your teeth to keep them clean. You wake up, you tell yourself you love yourself to keep your spirit bright. You can use Post-It notes filled with affirmations on the wall next to your bed or on your bathroom mirror to remind you to do this practice first thing.

8 Forgive

Forgiveness is one of the most powerful tools for self-love that you can do. Make a list of the people you need to forgive and create a ceremony of release for each person, one at a time. Write them a letter with everything you want to say. Then burn or bury the paper, letting go of that which has been heavy in your heart. You may feel a sense of deep release.

9 Marinate in Mantra

Use mantras to replace negative self-talk. Play them 24/7 in your living space, very softly, to infuse the energy into your body. Hunt online for mantras and musicians that you love. Keep an iPod playing while you are out of your living space so that when you walk back in, you are enveloped in positive vibrations.

10 Reclaim Your Mirrors

For many people with body acceptance challenges, mirrors can become terrifying. Take back the energy of your mirrors. Put positive self-affirming notes (like *I am Beautiful, I am Bountiful, I am Blissful*) on any mirrors that you pass by to remind you to be kind when you look into them. Use lipstick to draw hearts and write "Love" on them. Then change what you use your mirror to see. Use a mirror to look into your eyes to see your own soul rather than at your body in judgment. Gazing at your own eyes and saying "I love you" will shift something deep within. Let mirrors reflect your light back to you rather than take it away from you.

Ramdesh's Insight: Yogi Bhajan gave us a practice to help change our self-talk and become more aware of our inner dialogue. Sit before a mirror and talk out loud to yourself for 11 minutes a day. Just have a conscious dialogue, and notice the things that you think that you're unwilling to say aloud. Over time the dialogue begins to shift. This was a powerful practice for me in my early days of shifting my thinking—and I think you'll gain something from it, too.

11 Wear Your Inspiration

Wear inspiring jewelry. For example, I have a bracelet that says "Make Healthy Choices" that I wear around my wrist. I see it any time I eat or reach for food, and it helps me to remember to be kind to myself. You can also find a particular crystal whose energy you resonate with to wear. Not sure what to try? How about rose quartz? Wearing a peace of rose quartz can help you soften towards yourself and develop the habit of self-love.

12 Keep a Self-Love Journal

Keep a self-love journal; every night, write one loving thing about yourself in it. At the end of the 40 days, read them all back to yourself. Extend this practice for a whole year of self-love.

13 Write Self-Love Notes

Put notes where you're going to see them. I have a computer sleeve that is customized with the message "I love you! You're beautiful!" that I see every time I write, work, or check the internet. It keeps my love for myself at the forefront of my mind. A perfect place to leave a self-love note is on your fridge, to encourage you to be kind to yourself and your body. Learn to graciously accept these compliments you leave for yourself—and from others!

14 Give Yourself an Aura Sweep

Rub your hands together building up energy and then run your hands over your aura, keeping your hands about 3 inches from the body. Sweep your aura while visualizing any negative energy leaving and positive, healing energy replacing it.

15 Supercharge Your Water

Our bodies are mostly water, and yet we don't think of how much we are polluting our inner ocean! Rebalance yourself by making sure you are drinking high quality, alkaline water. Write positive words (Success! Healing! Self-Love!) or mantras (*Sat Nam! Waheguru!*) on your water bottle to charge the energy of your water with high vibration. Dehydration can cause emotional imbalances. Often if you are crying, or freaking out, and you are unsure of the reason, simply drinking a big glass of water can bring you back into alignment. Emotions are ruled by the water element, so make sure to keep yourself hydrated!

16 Host a Dance Party for Yourself

You don't need anyone to attend your dance party, just show up yourself! Turn up high vibrational music and dance and move your body with joy and primal power.

17 Cut Down on Caffeine

Caffeine stresses out your adrenals and your nervous system. Switch from coffee to green tea or herbal tea, or give up caffeine altogether. Once you detox, you won't need it to wake you up in the morning. You'll naturally feel more rested and vibrant.

18 Get a Good Night's Sleep

Make sure you are getting enough sleep. If you have trouble falling asleep, spend a few minutes with your legs up the wall before bedtime or try a few minutes of a pranayam like Left Nostril Breathing before bed.

19 Here Comes the Sun

Try sun-gazing! Watch the sunrise, allowing yourself to drink in prana from the sun through your eyes while the sun is still low in the horizon. There are many online resources and books to guide you through this practice; do some research and drink in the sun prana! Be cautious and respectful of this ancient practice by following the guidelines so that you don't hurt your eyes.

20 Be Passionate

To love your Body Temple means creating and sustaining healthy sexual relationships. Don't allow other people or yourself to disrespect you or dishonor you or your body. Sex is the most powerful, magical ritual we have, and it is an activity where you literally share your aura and absorb another's aura into your Arc Line. Make sure you want to take on the aura of your partner as you explore healthy, empowering sexual relationships. Developing an empowering sexuality is a part of loving yourself, but take care to spend time feeling your way into what truly empowers you.

21 Adorn Your Body

Wear things that make you feel beautiful. Often when we don't love our bodies, we tend to hide behind outfits that don't make us feel beautiful. Try a colorful scarf or a beautiful pair of earrings to pep up your outfit. Boost how you feel about yourself. Take it a step further and wear white for 40 days. White boosts your aura and expands your radiance. It is an energetically clear color that can make it easier to separate your energetic "stuff" from other people's by keeping your field strong. Yogi Bhajan said about wearing white: "It's a simple scientific fact that every piece of matter or material has a foot and a half Aura. Every animal has a three and a half foot Aura. Every human has a nine foot Aura. And if we wear the cotton and we wear the white, this color therapy gives us one extra foot of Aura. . . . It's pure color therapy, and it's called auric color therapy[36]."

22 Make a Joyful Sound

Explore sound therapy: crystal bowls, gong, metal bowls, flutes, drums, and more. All of these powerful musical instruments can help create a cellular vibration within you that is both deeply relaxing and transformational.

23 Create Art

Draw or paint a piece of art that represents your body in a loving way. Write or draw images and symbols that infuse you with love and power. I also love using coloring books. They take me back to my childhood for a simple, creative artistic experience. I travel with colored pencils and often color for a few minutes to shift my brain from work mode to play mode. Experiment!

24 Set Up a Love-Your-Body Altar

Creating a new altar is one of my favorite things to do. I have altars all over my house and refresh them regularly. Altars are a way of focusing your spiritual energy and intention. Creating an altar with a specific intention, such as a Self-Love altar, helps you call on the deeply healing power of self-love and invite more of it into your life.

You can create an altar from anything, the top of a dresser, a stool, a bench, a shelf, or even the floor. You can't build an altar incorrectly, but here are a few suggestions to try:

- Cover your altar with beautiful cloth that feels special to you. Place items on your altar that represent love to you: hearts, images of beautiful goddesses, candles. Add a photo of yourself to the altar alongside everything that represents love to you.
- Find a few sacred stones that resonate with you: rose quartz for love, malachite for healing the wounds of heart and body, quartz to amplify your intentions, amethyst for spiritual clarity; these are just a few that you could seek out.
- Write words of support down on paper and place them on your altar to inspire you, such as Beauty, Joy, Healing, Transformation, Love.
- Place flowers or anything that represents love and beauty to you on your altar.
- Dedicate your altar to yourself and your body with a prayer of intention such as "I dedicate this altar to my body and my heart. With these words, it is activated with the intention of love and healing."
- Regularly smudge your altar with smoke from sage or Palo Santo to keep the energy clear.

25 Spend a Day with No Comparisons

Spend one entire day without comparing yourself to anyone else. Don't compare yourself to your friends, family, co-workers, or celebrities. Allow yourself to just be who you are and let that be good enough. If you slip up, start again the next day and go a full 24 hours without comparison. You are already enough!

26 Try a Writing Exercise

Yogi Bhajan suggested a powerful writing exercise to journal truthfully with yourself and your hidden side. Be honest with the paper about your eating disorders or your self-harming rituals, or write about an aspect of yourself that you are longing to share with the world, but keep hidden. Be honest and do the work! Write without fear. You never have to show anyone what you've written.

"Tonight sit down, work on yourself and find out about that little you. You will do yourself the greatest service if you can find out about your hidden self; put it on paper and hand it over. If you'll honestly write it down, you'll get rid of a lot of that hidden self, and it will interfere much less in your life. Do you understand? Try to be extremely honest; I know it is difficult, but it's a very worthy cause for your own progress. I would like you to understand, this is one time in your life that you should be very truthful with yourself."

~ *Yogi Bhajan*

27 Go for a Walk in Nature

There's nothing more healing than the power of nature. Get outside. Breathe the fresh air and feel the sunshine on your face. Take your shoes off and try "earthing," which connects your bioelectric field with that of the Earth directly. Hike in the woods, walk along the river, jog on the beach. Many Native traditions say that the answer to any question can be found in nature. A stone does not hurt itself when it is shaped differently than it would like; why should you? Be at peace with yourself and experience yourself as a part of the natural world. It is profound.

28 Take a Cold Shower

Ishnaan, or cold showers, is a form of hydrotherapy that activates the immune system and energizes the body. Before getting into a cold shower, cover your body in almond oil. Then step into the cold water and vigorously rub the body for a few minutes until the water doesn't feel as cold. Make sure to massage your armpits and breast area. Chanting a mantra like *Waheguru* can help keep your mind focused. Cold showers will increase the oxygenation of your blood and keep you looking young and beautiful! (**Note:** *Cold showers are not recommended for menstruating or pregnant women.*)

29 Check Your Minerals

One of the kindest things you can do for yourself is to have a doctor check your vitamin and mineral levels. You could be low on Vitamin B_{12}, magnesium, iron, calcium, or Vitamin D among others. Having a low mineral level in the body makes you feel awful, and it's hard to love your body when it hurts. A few years ago, my body hurt constantly. It was hard to sit, stand, or get up. I felt like I was 100 years old;

everything ached, and everything was hard to do. I had my mineral levels checked, and I was incredibly low on Vitamin D, which can lead to cancer, bone loss, and more. After an aggressive program to get my numbers back up, I felt better within a few weeks. I couldn't believe I had come to accept pain and discomfort as my body's normal for nearly a year. In fact, well-being is your natural state. Do your body a kindness and make sure it has everything it needs to serve you.

30 Healing Baths

Take a ritual healing bath. Find some alone time, light some candles and infuse your warm water with things that will re-mineralize and relax your body. My favorite healing bath is Epsom salts, hydrogen peroxide, and baking soda sprinkled with some lavender oil. The Epsom salts infuse my body with healing magnesium, and the other ingredients help to diffuse the effects of radiation from cell phones and Wi-Fi networks. Lavender oil is incredibly relaxing. The bottom line is you will feel marvelous. Play some of your favorite healing mantra music to infuse every cell of you with healing and love.

31 Body Image Acceptance Meditation

I have recorded many guided visualizations and meditations designed for those who have a way to go to accepting and loving their bodies. Play them. Every day. Go on the journeys with me, following my voice, repeat the affirmations. They will help you; they are a guided tour out of the darkness.

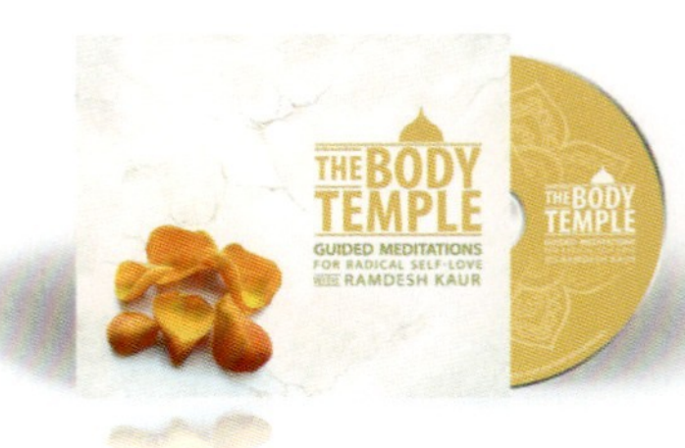

32 Holy Rollers

You might think this suggestion is funny, but it is absolutely one that I use for myself and I love it! I buy essential oil rollers and use them to write loving words on my body. I take a lavender essential oil roller, which is like a ballpoint pen that has essential oils instead of ink, and write "love," "beauty," "peace," "harmony," "enough," all over my body. Not only does the lovely scent relax and uplift me, but there is an incredible power to giving yourself a temporary tattoo of light and love. In addition to Lavender, Palmarosa and Angelica are essential oils that support eating disorder recovery. If you prefer, you could try this technique using a natural eyeliner, melted chocolate, or other forms of body-safe paint.

33 Crown Yourself

One of the ways that I keep my head on straight, especially when I feel like my thinking is starting to get out of whack, is to wrap my head in a headscarf or turban. Wearing a head covering provides a sense of containment, clarity of thought, and focus. It tunes the neurological system and protects your delicate intuition centers from other people's energy. It also feels like a crown. When I wrap my head, it straightens my posture, and helps remind me to watch my thoughts, because they create my reality. You might try it for yourself, and see if it has similar effects for you.

34 Attitude of Gratitude

Spend a few minutes thinking about things you love about your body. If this is hard and feels too difficult right now, then think of a day in your life that was magical where you did something active like walking, swimming, or dancing, and thank your body for giving you that experience. Begin to feel gratitude for your body for pumping your blood, making new cells, regulating your temperature, and so much more. The body does so many things for us every single day. Begin to thank it for what it does do well, and then let your gratitude spill out. Feel grateful for all the blessings of your life. List the people you love, those who love you, the best experiences you've had. Develop an attitude of gratitude. You will attract more good experiences and good feelings to you when you live in gratitude. If you are in the thick of an eating disorder right now, see if you can go one day without restricting or purging or bingeing. And then be grateful for that one day. Live your way into such a state of outrageous self-love that you are grateful for all the hard stuff, all the angry, critical thoughts you've ever had, because they've been such enormous teachers that eventually brought you onto the path of self-love. Start small or big with gratitude. It's a muscle; lift as much as you can, then push yourself a little further. When you live with an attitude of gratitude, goodness rushes in to flood your life.

35 Go on a Pilgrimage

There is such magic in taking a spiritual pilgrimage. For thousands of years, humans have found meaning in journeying to a place where miracles are said to occur. Maybe you would like to go to one of the holy cities on the Ganga River, or to the Golden Temple in Amritsar, or to the Lourdes Chapel in France, or walk the Camino de Santiago. It doesn't matter what your pilgrimage is; it must be entirely unique to you and what calls your soul. The teachings you need lie in the journey. There will be stress, but it will be the kind of stress that calls you to rise above it and move beyond reactivity. There may even be miracles. I have found great healing in India, in Mayan Temples, and in chapels in Italy. Part of the power of pilgrimage is to remove you from your everyday life and carve out a period of time that is dedicated to the relationship between you and the Infinite. If you cannot go on a pilgrimage to somewhere far away, find somewhere magical nearby and go there. You might find a pond or a park that you can declare a place of pilgrimage, and you journey there, by car or foot, and come to a divine appointment with your soul. Miracles are far more common than you think. Go get one.

36 Make Music

Find a chanting group, go to a kirtan concert, play your guitar, or bang on the pots in your own kitchen. Making music is one of the greatest tools we have for experiencing joy. If you aren't a musician, turn on a recording and sing along. If you haven't done this in a while, or maybe even since kindergarten, why haven't you? Make a joyful sound and feel the resonance within. You are made up of sound and light dancing together. Music is a part of who you are; let it call back the bits of your soul you have forgotten along your way.

37 Laugh More

Get the giggles. Watch funny movies. Call up a hysterical friend. Exercise your funny bone. Laughter has seriously epic healing power. It's a mood stabilizer and an immune booster. Have fun. This is your life; why not enjoy it?

38 Say Three Good Things to Yourself

Here's a great rule: anytime you catch yourself saying something negative about yourself, you have to immediately follow it up with three good things. You have to say nice things to yourself in order to undo the energetic imprint of the mean things you've said. It doesn't matter if your unkind words were out loud or silent, you still have to say three positive things in their place. You may find this gets so tedious that it is easier to just quit being a jerk to yourself, and at the very least, you will become accustomed to being kinder to yourself.

39 Don't Take Yourself So Seriously

Your whole life cannot be about your eating disorder, or your weight, or your looks, or even your healing from all these things. You have to find balance. Read a good book. See a movie. Call a friend. Shop online. Learn sign language, or even Chinese! Don't let your challenges define you. Don't let your issues with your body define your life. Don't take everything so seriously. It is possible to have a life that is glorious and delicious and fun. No matter what has happened to you and no matter what you are dealing with, joy is your natural state. Let yourself get back to your joy; stop being so hard on yourself and quit taking yourself so seriously.

40 Pray

When the going gets tough, the tough get to praying. You don't need to be religious or relate to God in order to pray. If you have a tradition that makes you feel good—great! But it's not a requirement. In fact, I'd suggest you release your notions of what God is or isn't and reach out to the Infinite. Allow a power greater than your own to guide your life. Ask for help. Pray. Trust that guidance is coming. Pray however feels right to you. Saturate yourself in the Divine. It works, and it heals.

THE END OF THE BEGINNING

"Self-love is the best love."

~ Yogi Bhajan
April 25, 1969

There will be no end to your journey. You will need to practice self-love, self-care, and self-honoring for the rest of your life. To overcome an eating disorder and fall in love with your body can be a life-long journey. To cultivate a deep reservoir of self-esteem and learn to love yourself and your Body Temple, no matter what, can be a challenging task. But consider this: what a joy it is to fall in love with your Self, body and soul, every day. What a joy it is to live a life of constantly falling in love. You deserve it. This journey of love is for you and your precious Body Temple worships you for taking it.

Postscript

The day will come when you finally heal from your challenges and wake up to the realization that you have fallen madly in love with yourself, with your spirit, and with the world around you. You will come to realize that we live in an age of the awakening of human consciousness. After a moment of bliss, you will remember that there are others who have not woken up. When you are ready, pass your love along, and help them on their journeys, too. Pay it forward, and help someone else wake up to their beauty. Care for yourself. Be kind to yourself. Live with mindful compassion. Then teach someone else to do the same. Sat Nam.

"Some of you who are sitting here will become great Teachers of the Age of Aquarius. You must understand that you have to build your character first. Care for yourself, be kind to yourself, be compassionate to yourself. That is what you have to do."

~ Yogi Bhajan, April 23, 1997

Acknowledgments

This book would not have happened without the vision and faith of Karan Khalsa. A thousand thank you's to this amazing woman and soul sister! I am also so grateful to Ram Dass, Simranpreet, and everyone at Spirit Voyage who lent support and hard work along the way. A special chanupa ceremony of thanks to Ram Dass for for his music production, musical annotations, project management, and copious emotional support. Gratitude to Gurusurya, for her incredible photography, to Ditta and Biljana for their beautiful design, and to my editors Sahib-Amar and Sat Purkh. Thanks as well to Dr. Kathy Milano, who wrote the Foreword, for her grace-filled clinical perspective. A big hug to Anne Novak, for her encyclopedia-like brain that always came to my rescue late at night, finding sources and making suggestions. I am also deeply grateful to the amazing women of Jala Yoga in West Virginia, and their fearless leader Christa Mastrangelo Joyce, who so selflessly gave their time to this project and became the Body Temple family. And I must thank my own family, my inspiring mother Rev. Dr. Carol, my supportive father Greg, and my amazing sister Arielle. I wouldn't be who and where I am today without them. A most honorable mention to my canine angel Suki, who passed away during the final stages of writing this book, but who faithfully stayed by my side every day she could and who lived through so much of my journey with me. Finally, I bow before my extraordinary husband Harnam, who held my hand through the writing of this project, encouraged me to be creative and brave at every step, and made me a million cups of self-love tea.

Endnotes

CHAPTER 3

1 Sullivan, P. F. (July 1995). *American Journal of Psychiatry, 152*(7), 1073-1074.

2 Wade, T. D., Keski-Rahkonen A., & Hudson, J. (2011). Epidemiology of eating disorders. In M. Tsuang & M. Tohen (Eds.), *Textbook in Psychiatric Epidemiology* (3rd ed., pp. 343-360). New York: Wiley.

3 Substance Abuse and Mental Health Services Administration (SAMHSA), The Center for Mental Health Services (CMHS), Offices of the U.S. Department of Health and Human Services.

4 Wade, T. D., Keski-Rahkonen, A., & Hudson, J. (2011). Epidemiology of eating disorders. In M. Tsuang & M. Tohen (Eds.), *Textbook in Psychiatric Epidemiology* (3rd ed., pp. 343-360). New York: Wiley.

5 Neumark-Sztainer, D. (2005). *I'm, Like, SO Fat!* New York: The Guilford Press.

6 Noordenbox, G. (2002). Characteristics and treatment of patients with chronic eating disorders. *International Journal of Eating Disorders, 10*, 15-29.

6b Wildes, J. E., et. al. (October 2008). *Psychiatry Res., 161*(1), 51–58.

7 Mellin, L., McNutt, S., Hu, Y., Schreiber, G. B., Crawford, P., & Obarzanek, E. (1991). A longitudinal study of the dietary practices of black and white girls 9 and 10 years old at enrollment: The NHLBI growth and health study. *Journal of Adolescent Health*, 23-37.

8 Carlat, D. J., Camargo, C. A., Jr., & Herzog, D. B. (1997). Review of bulimia nervosa in males. *American Journal of Psychiatry, 154.*

9 Russell, C. J., & Keel, P. K. (2002). Homosexuality as a specific risk factor for eating disorders in men. *International Journal of Eating Disorders, 31*, 300-308.

10 The National Institute of Mental Health. *Eating disorders: Facts about eating disorders and the search for solutions.* Pub No. 01-4901. Accessed Feb. 2002.

11 Crow, S. J., Peterson, C. B., Swanson, S. A., Raymond, N. C., Specker, S., Eckert, E. D., & Mitchell, J. E. (2009). Increased mortality in bulimia nervosa and other eating disorders. *American Journal of Psychiatry, 166*, 1342-1346.

12 The Renfrew Center Foundation for Eating Disorders. (2002). *Eating Disorders 101 Guide: A Summary of Issues, Statistics and Resources* (rev. 2003).

13 Bhajan, Yogi. Restraining compulsive overeating. In *Praana, Praanee, Praanayam.* Kundalini Research Institute. (Original quote KWTC, 1979)

14 Bratman, Steven, M.D. (October 1997). Orthorexia. *Yoga Journal.*

15 Bjornsson, A. S., Didie, E. R., & Phillips, K. A. (2010). Body dysmorphic disorder. *Dialogues Clin Neurosci, 12*(2), 221–232.

CHAPTER 4

16 There are many references for the collected teachings of Kundalini Yoga as Taught by Yogi Bhajan. Bhajan, Yogi. (2007). *The Aquarian Teacher.* Kundalini Research Institute (4th ed.)

17 Ibid.

18 Ibid.

19 Bhajan, Yogi. (1988). *The Mind: Its Projections and Multiple Facets.* Kundalini Research Institute.

CHAPTER 7

20 Bhajan, Yogi. (2007). *The Aquarian Teacher.* Kundalini Research Institute (4th ed.)

21 Khalsa, Bibiji Inderjit Kaur. (2014). *Mantra: Personal Guidance through the Power of the Word* (p. 154). Kundalini Research Institute.

22 Ibid., p. 95.

23 Bhajan, Yogi. (2007). *The Aquarian Teacher.* Kundalini Research Institute (4th ed., p. 87).

24 Ibid., p. 86.

25 Ibid., p. 82.

26 Ibid., p. 86.

27 Khalsa, Bibiji Inderjit Kaur. (2014). *Mantra: Personal Guidance through the Power of the Word* (p. 95). Kundalini Research Institute.

28 Bhajan, Yogi. (2007). *The Aquarian Teacher.* Kundalini Research Institute (4th ed., p. 82).

29 Ibid., p. 84.

30 Khalsa, Harijot Kaur. "Exercises for the Heart Center." In *Reaching Me in Me. (*Original Yogi Bhajan lecture date: April 11, 1984).

31 Khalsa, Bibiji Inderjit Kaur. (2014). *Mantra: Personal Guidance through the Power of the Word* (p. 268). Kundalini Research Institute.

32 Bhajan, Yogi. (2007). *The Aquarian Teacher.* Kundalini Research Institute (4th ed., p. 153).

33 From the personal notes of Guru Prem Singh and Simran Kaur.

34 Khalsa, Bibiji Inderjit Kaur. (2014). *Mantra: Personal Guidance through the Power of the Word* (p. 126). Kundalini Research Institute.

35 From the personal notes of Hari Charan Kaur Khalsa.

36 From *I Am A Woman* Lecture Series, January 1, 1969.

Bibliography

Bhajan, Yogi. (1989). *The inner workout manual.* Santa Cruz, NM: Kundalini Research Institute (KRI).

Bhajan, Yogi, & Khalsa, Gurucharan S. (Ed.). (1998). *The mind: Its projections and multiple facets*. Santa Cruz, NM: KRI.

Bhajan, Yogi. (2007). *Kundalini Yoga: Sadhana guidelines* (2nd ed.). Santa Cruz, NM: KRI.

Bhajan, Yogi. (2007). *The Aquarian teacher* (4th ed.). Santa Cruz, NM: KRI.

Bhajan, Yogi. (2009). *I am a woman: Selected lectures*. Santa Cruz, NM: KRI.

Bhajan, Yogi. (2010). *Transformation: Mastering the self (Vol. 1)*. Santa Cruz, NM: KRI.

Bhajan, Yogi. (2010). *Transformation: Serving the infinite (Vol. 2)*. Santa Cruz, NM: KRI.

Khalsa, Bibiji Inderjit K. (2014). *Mantra: Personal guidance through the power of word.* Santa Cruz, NM: KRI.

Khalsa, Gurucharan S. (2012). *The 21 stages of meditation*. Santa Cruz, NM: KRI.

Khalsa, Harijot K. (2002). *Reaching me in me.* Santa Cruz, NM: KRI.

Khalsa, Mukta K. (2008). *Meditations for addictive behavior*. Santa Cruz, NM: KRI.

Khalsa, Nam K., & Khalsa, Siri Atma S. (2013). *Divine relationships: Two bodies, one soul.* Los Angeles, CA: Yogic Reality.

Khalsa, Sat Purkh K. (Ed.). (2009). *I am a woman: Essential kriyas*. Santa Cruz, NM: KRI.

Khalsa, Sat Purkh K. (Ed.). (2013). *Kriya: Yoga sets, meditations and classic kriyas*. Santa Cruz, NM: KRI.

Lumpkin, Nirmal, & Khalsa, Japa K. (2015). *Enlightened bodies: Exploring physical and subtle human anatomy*. Santa Cruz, NM: KRI.

Seibel, Machelle M., & Khalsa, Hari K. (2002). *A woman's book of yoga: Embracing our natural life cycles*. New York, NY: Avery Penguin Putnam.

Shannahoff-Khalsa, David S. (2006). *Kundalini Yoga meditation: Techniques specific for psychiatric disorders, couples therapy, and personal growth*. New York, NY: W.W. Norton.

Glossary

A

Arcline
One of the Ten Bodies. A thin halo-like arc that goes from ear to ear. Women have an additional Arcline that goes across the breasts. It is an energetic field that relates to destiny, potential, and spiritual power.

Asana
Posture. Each posture affects the physical and mental bodies in a particular way.

Aura
One of the Ten Bodies. A radiant field of energy around the entire body. Its strength, which relates to brightness and size, determines vitality. It contains the chakra system and is also considered the Eighth Chakra.

B

Bhanda
Body locks. They stimulate the flow of energy through the body and promote proper alignment.

Bij
Root part of a mantra that has additional meaning and resonance, usually one syllable.

Breath of Fire
A foundational breathing exercise in Kundalini Yoga with many health benefits.

Brow Point
Also called the Third Eye or Third Eye Point. It is the point between the eyebrows and is the seat of intuition. It corresponds to the Sixth Chakra and relates to the functioning of the pituitary gland.

C

Chakra
Wheel or energy centers of the body. There are seven main centers plus the Aura as the Eighth Chakra. They are centers of consciousness that hold within them certain values and specific energies. Kundalini energy rises through the chakras.

Chant
Singing. Often repeating a mantra.

D

Drishti
Eye focus. It means pure seeing and helps to direct the flow of energy within the body.

N

Negative Mind
One of the Three Minds. A protective and defensive aspect of the mind.

Neutral Mind
One of the Three Minds. It judges the information from the Positive and Negative Minds and weighs them equally. A highly important aspect of the mind for clarity and awareness.

P

Positive Mind
One of the Three Minds. A projective and magnifying aspect of the mind.

Prana
Life force energy.

Pranayam
Conscious breath control or exercises.

S

Sadhana
A discipline of spiritual practice. Often refers to morning practice.

Sat Nam
True Name or Vibration of Truth. The seed of truth. A common mantra, it is also used as a greeting by Kundalini Yogis.

Seva
Selfless service.

T

Ten Bodies
Humans are said to have Ten Bodies, or vehicles of the spirit. They include the Soul Body, the three Mental Bodies (Negative, Positive, and Neutral Minds), the Physical Body, the Arcline, the Aura, the Pranic Body, the Subtle Body, and the Radiant Body. Each corresponds to a different aspect of the human or spiritual experience.

Third Eye or Third Eye Point
Also called the Brow Point. An intuition center.

Y

Yoga
Union of the spirit and body.

Yogi
One who practices yoga and has achieved a state of self-mastery.

Yogini
Sometimes used to refer to a female yogi.

Resources

To study with me or learn more about my work see my website.
www.Ramdesh.com

To check out more Body Temple resources and bonus material, see Spirit Voyage.
www.SpiritVoyage.com/BodyTemple

For more information on Kundalini Yoga and all of your yogic lifestyle needs, including beautiful music to practice along with, Spirit Voyage is my go-to resource.
www.SpiritVoyage.com

To find a Kundalini Yoga teacher near you, head to the International Kundalini Yoga Teachers Association.
www.IKYTA.org

To join a large gathering of Kundalini yogis, discover Sat Nam Fest or Summer/Winter Solstice.
www.SatNamFest.com or **www.3HO.org**

Read the teachings of Yogi Bhajan directly and search the archives of his classes and lectures at the Library of Teachings.
www.LibraryofTeachings.com

To learn more about becoming a Kundalini Yoga teacher, head to the Kundalini Research Institute.
www.KRI.org

Learn more about my husband Harnam (Tony Zatzick) and his work with art, creativity, yoga, and music.
www.HarnamTonyZatzick.com

To join me on Yoga & Seva Retreats, or to contribute to charitable causes around the world, I invite you to learn more about Sat Nam Foundation.
www.SatNamFoundation.org

About the Author

Ramdesh Kaur is a KRI Certified Kundalini Yoga and Meditation teacher who has taught throughout the world, from the foothills of the Himalayas to the suburbs of New Jersey. She holds a Master's Degree from the Courtauld Institute in London and a Bachelor's Degree from the University of Virginia.

She is the host of *Spirit Voyage Radio with Ramdesh* on Unity FM, a weekly podcast that brings mantra and meditation to over 300,000 listeners each year. In addition to *The Body Temple: Kundalini Yoga for Body Acceptance, Eating Disorders, and Radical Self-Love*, she is also the co-author of *Yoga and Mantras for a Whole Heart* with Karan Khalsa, and has many best-selling guided meditation albums that create deeply healing and accessible meditation experiences for all.

At the age of 9, Ramdesh fell ill with a life-threatening disease. After weeks in a coma, she woke up with a deeper sense of her connection to her spirit. Now deaf from her illness, she struggled to fit into a world driven by external appearances. The medications used to save her life also gave her sudden and severe weight gain, which developed into a lifetime of eating disorders and addictive behaviors as she attempted to fit in. In her early 20s, she had a series of cochlear implant surgeries that restored her hearing.

Searching for the connection to the Divine she first felt during her coma, she began studying many different spiritual paths until she found Kundalini Yoga and the yogic teachings of Yogi Bhajan. Through her devotion to this practice, she healed her addictions and eating disorders, and developed a deep sense of self-love.

A global citizen and awakened heart, her name means *One who sees the land of God everywhere, in all places and all peoples*. She serves on the Board of Directors of the Sat Nam Foundation and leads Seva Retreats in India and Nepal. She has lived in the US, India, France, Italy, and England, and now shares her life with her husband Harnam, an artist, musician, and yogi.

www.ramdesh.com